Jack Temple's healing methods focus on removing toxins from the body and balancing energy to encourage inner healing. A veteran contributor to *Here's Health* magazine, he has been in practise for over twenty years and runs a successful clinic in Surrey, England. His mission is to establish the Jack Temple Healing Academy to pass on his knowledge and techniques to new generations of practitioners.

JACK TEMPLE

BOOK 1
The Healer
*the extraordinary
story of Jack Temple*

FINDHORN
Press

First Findhorn Press edition 2002

ISBN 1-899171-44-4

British Library Cataloguing-in-Publication Data.
A catalogue record for this book is available
from the British Library.

Cover Design by Thierry Bogliolo
Printed and bound in Great Britain by
J. W. Arrowsmith Ltd, Bristol

Published by
Findhorn Press
The Press Building, The Park
Findhorn, Forres IV36 3TY
Scotland, UK
tel 01309 690582
fax 01309 690036
email info@findhornpress.com
findhornpress.com

Contents

Contents

Foreword

I first heard about Jack through a friend of mine whose mother was a patient at his clinic in Surrey, England. I was in Spain at the time and I felt I needed help. One of my main problems was that a lot of my energy was blocked by slimming pills that I had taken in the past. These can be a real danger to so many people. I knew instinctively what was wrong with me and the first thing I did when I got back to the UK was to go and see him.

My first impression of him was that I couldn't believe his age. He is the best example of someone who practises what he preaches. He bounced into the room like a rubber ball and I had to ask him three times how old he was. I now know Jack is an extraordinary man who is more energetic about life than lots of younger people.

Now I visit Jack's clinic regularly, but towards the end of 1997 I was working most of the time in America and I felt that my health had deteriorated because I was unable to see him. My life is very pressurized and stressful, and at that time I had to deal with a lot of negativity from the British media. I spend a lot of time travelling by air and am vulnerable to changes in climate and environment which can be very draining.

It's not that I would say I am reliant or dependent on Jack, but I feel I am in need of his ability to heal. By helping me clear my energy blockages Jack has given me strength to be able to think clearly, and this has helped me enormously. Often I have come into his office feeling very depressed and low, and walked out later having taken an awful lot from him.

Jack's path is unique. It means he has to take on criticism from medical and other people who disagree with what he does. I believe wholeheartedly in him, but, as always with anything different from the norm, people are often prejudiced rather than open-minded. I recommend him to many people, but there are those who are cynical or afraid to try his methods of treatment. Jack has helped to improve the lives of many of his patients, as the case studies in this book will show. I am now stronger than I was thanks to Jack, and I am 100 per cent behind him and his work. If there weren't people around like Jack Temple who are prepared to stand up for what they believe in and fight for it, where would the world be?

Sarah, Duchess of York

Introduction

There are turning points in each of our lives, although at the time we seldom realize the importance of the apparently chance meeting, impulsive decision or casual choice. People sometimes talk of bolts from the blue and flashes of inspiration, and no doubt that happens to others. My turning point had no dramatic tension at all – and yet it motivated me towards the course I have pursued for nearly twenty-five years now.

It began in a quiet, almost mundane way, early in the 1970s. Blanche, my wife, had been unwell for a while and I was taking time away from the business to look after her; we were both virtually pensioners, she nearing retirement from her civil service job and I a successful Surrey market gardener beginning to think about slowing down a little and enjoying a peaceful old age. After thirty years of tending the same fields and observing the seasons the soil had got under my skin as well as my fingernails, and I had no plans to completely close down my business and move away – merely a wish to take things easier, see more of my family and friends, to enjoy the fruits of my work in a comfortable retirement.

At London's first Festival of Mind and Body I was exhibiting organic cultivation products, but I felt free to wander and look at the other stands where all manner of what were later to become known as New Age ideas were being demonstrated or displayed. At the time a good many of them were dismissed as post-hippy gimmicks and it amuses me now to see how much of this 'cranky' stuff has become accepted and respected by more conventional bodies. At the Aetherius Society stand, where health foods and pendulums for self-dowsing were exhibited, I saw someone dowsing to see whether they had a tissue salt deficiency. Most of those who had gathered around that day wouldn't have known what a tissue salt was, but the demonstrator continued with good humour. Then others were invited to dowse themselves and I watched, fascinated. With some people the pendulum barely moved and, almost in response to a challenge, I couldn't resist testing it myself. To my surprise the pendulum whirled and swirled like a dervish when I picked it up although I'd made no effort to make it move.

I had little knowledge of or interest in dowsing but I was curious now. Why did mine whizz about like that? Might it be responding to some force in my hand? Still puzzled, I mentioned this to Blanche when I returned home that day and she almost chided me for not buying one. I had to remind her that neither of us had been impressed by the dowsing of a local osteopath when we'd visited him after her illness had begun to worry us. But Blanche was insistent and the next day I returned to the Festival and bought my first pendulum. As an established organic gardener and a regular contributor to *Here's Health* magazine I had seen more than my fair share of crazy ideas first advanced and then forgotten, so my interest was not that of a wide-eyed naive innocent.

Soon a fellow journalist, observing my growing interest in dowsing, suggested I spoke to Bruce MacManaway, a pioneering dowsing healer who worked mostly in Scotland but who treated patients in London several times a month. Bruce very kindly asked me to visit him and even let me dowse a patient he was examining that day.

With no more training then than a study of a short booklet which explained that the dowser silently asks questions of the pendulum as it is held over a patient and notes the activity of the device on a scale of one to ten, I dowsed under Bruce's guidance and offered him my opinions. To my surprise he told me that I was spot on and asked me to help him. I worked with Bruce and his patients for four days a month over the next year, learning about many aspects of his healing. Then he said, 'Right. Out you go. You are a healer.' I was aghast, almost frightened, and reminded him that I didn't have any qualifications. Bruce snorted. 'You're a healer, Jack. You don't need qualifications. Go out and heal.'

Blanche agreed that I should do just that. Already one or two people on my organic gardening courses had asked if I could look at health problems, the news had somehow spread . . . and that is how I became a dowsing healer.

I have no conventional medical qualifications and many have tried to mock me. This sometimes masks their fear of the unknown or misunderstood. But patients' testimonies about the remission of their pain or stress – I do not use the word 'cure' because nothing is certain – inspire me to work on and to further explore the potential of plants and the organic power of the earth in which they grow all over the world.

It is this same earth which nourishes us all. Every fibre, every bone, every drop of body fluid derives from the soil. Human remains have fed the earth over thousands of centuries and it retains enormous life-giving forces. Think of fossil stones which bear the imprint of a leaf or ammonite sea creature, perhaps on the outside or deep within when cracked open. The remains of everything that ever lived, human, animal and vegetable are mulched down, deep into our soil. The DNA of bones, stones, leaves, bark and branches as well as that of insect, human and animal remains has fed its force into the earth. Every hillock in a wood or meadow flowering with bracken or bluebell, every raised copse, probably represents the shape or shapes of a tree or trees which stood for centuries and then fell, centuries ago.

I simply try to observe all these and then attempt to identify a patient's needs and channel an essential essence towards their problem – usually in the form of homeopathic tablets containing plant and/or mineral extracts taped to the relevant, responsive part of their body. This may not be at the actual place of pain or distress but upon one of the body's meridian lines which always link to that source.

Every one of the plants so central to my work grows in our earth, which is nourished by crops, weeds, mould, droppings, human and animal and insect remains, minerals and all the other detritus which has been steeped into it. Only some of that detritus is harmful – most of it is benign, but I must always be watchful. All these remains are broken down by the myriads of bacteria that are always present in beneficial soil ready to be recycled as food for the next phase of growth.

I cannot overstress the importance of the soil, loam or clay from which most ingredients for my remedies spring – whether in plant or ancient rock and mineral form. Something laid to rest hundreds or even thousands of years ago, far beneath the grass where our feet tread, will influence the character of plants growing or stones found today. Remember that the roots of every plant and flower stretch down far deeper than the fistful of tufts you may tug from your garden.

There are also channels of everlasting energy coming to the

earth's surface from hundreds of feet down. I have discovered that the radius of these channels is only about six inches. To my complete amazement, when I dowsed one channel of energy the pendulum swung left; and then a hundred miles away I found a channel that made it swing right. I concluded that they are actually made to fit the human body. The left part of the body is what we call the negative part – the pendulum swings round the negative on the left – and the right part is positive – the pendulum swings round on the right.

This power in the soil can be harnessed in homeopathic liquid form. If a fragment of this magnetized soil is diluted in a homeopathic fluid it can supply gentle energy. The patient holds the left energy phial in the left hand and the right energy phial in the right and finds that a steady flow of healing energy is soaked into the body. It takes about five minutes for all the stored energy to be absorbed and about half an hour for the liquid to recharge itself. Patients who have taken these bottles home have found them very beneficial when they're in need of recharging. The energy is everlasting, and I also use this wonder fluid to deal with the exhaustion sometimes suffered by those who sit too often in front of a computer screen, which can limit vital iron absorption. A drop of the appropriate right and left energy liquids is placed inside each shoe, and patients tell me that after this their energy levels for work remain constant all day, with no afternoon flagging.

And so to the pendulum, so central to my work as a healer. My heavy silver dowser may swing to the source of pain or ailment and suggest the point of the body where treatment may effect recovery or at least relief. Then it will advise me about which plant- or mineral-based remedy might work best. And because my dowser reacts specifically and uniquely to the individual there can be few generalizations in describing my work.

The pendulum swings and, yes, life does go on. It goes on in the trees, the clouds above them, in bark, in leaf mould and compost, in stones washed up by tides and in the seas and oceans, in the enormousness of mountains and the tiniest insect corpse or flower petal where a bee once rested and deposited a copy of its DNA. Only think of amber, that prized and beautiful resin created by the insect life upon aged pine trees' secretions, and you will understand. Animal life is compacted and impacted in all these natural features. Human healing can be sourced there.

In recent years the scope of my work has been broadened, almost revolutionized. Firstly it is by my colleague's skill in iridology. Her reports enable me to read a 'map' of someone's health through a specially analysed photograph of their iris. Secondly, a deeper understanding of patients' auras has become central to my work. Now I can see more clearly not only what tendencies towards illness anyone is likely to have inherited but also what problems may lie ahead for them, problems I can often neutralize before they even attack. Later chapters deal with these two extraordinary breakthroughs.

You may wish to know a little more about me and how I came to adopt these beliefs – many of which were nurtured, if not quite established, some time before I bought that first pendulum.

Looking back I can see other turning points, pivotal moments, spins of the wheel that lead to where I am today. The first was when I was a very frail young man at the start of the Second World War.

I was born in 1917 in the East End of London, where my father was a master tailor. I was the fourth of six brothers. My blood is a fusion of Jewish and Polish although, through my dowsing, I have learned that I derive more from ancient ancestors on the Isle of Skye 46,000 years ago. My bones and blood still carry the DNA of hundreds of forebears and so do yours. It really isn't such an extraordinary idea: all gardeners understand the use and importance of compost and mulch, and the human tissue and bone fragments which feed wilder soil are much the same. Knowing this I can use my pendulum first to dowse for areas of imbalance and then to decipher which plant and mineral remedies might best help any patient – including myself.

When William Wordsworth wrote

I think that I shall never see
A thing as lovely as a tree

he may not have been expressing quite the same awe that I feel about those roots which take nourishment from the depths and soul of the soil, but we do have something in common. A tree is a perfect, visible expression of natural growth, evolution, symmetry and strength – just as the human body can be. That a tree is always beautiful is another matter altogether. We all have different perceptions and notions of human beauty and my work is seldom concerned with these. It is health, calm and well-being that I strive for with my patients.

As a child I was blessed with little of that. Loving as they were, my parents were harassed, money was always short in such a big family and not much was understood in those days about the importance of nutrition. Like many children of my generation I suffered from rickets – a condition which did not observe class barriers. King George VI spent much of his early childhood, just like me, with his legs strapped to painful splints. As well as the bone disorder which had affected my legs, I had endless stomach, bowel and nutritional problems and was in and out of hospital every year until I was nineteen. It can't be hard to imagine how distressing this was for a young man who might have wanted to join a park football team or keep up to scratch with his schoolwork.

Of necessity, having sadly had to abandon other ambitions and dreams I might have cherished, I embarked on a routine clerical job. It didn't exactly make me feel claustrophobic or too depressed because now that I was earning some money and was drawn to the countryside I could afford to get out there at weekends. My health was improving by now, so I could enjoy walking, camping and youth-hostelling. The course of my life was being shaped.

I still had some hopes of catching up educationally and I enrolled in courses to improve my English and, at the Regent Street Polytechnic, to study electrical engineering. But these plans, too, shifted when the Second World War broke out.

I longed to join the navy but, still rather frail, I was examined and rejected by no fewer than seven doctors. All agreed that I was fit for nothing, but I longed to serve my country and was devastated when I received a hateful little brown card which declared I was exempted from any form of military service. But the next day another one of those turning points occurred. I heard the Home Secretary, Herbert Morrison, broadcast on BBC radio. He said that Britain's second line of defence was food production for its people and forces. I resolved at once to make my contribution to the war effort on the land.

We barely grew a weed in the tiny backyard behind the family house. I knew nothing of agriculture. But I decided to leave London for Surrey and offer my services to a farmer there. I actually asked him not to pay me the going rate for land-workers because I was such a novice, and a rather weedy one at that. I wanted to help but I wanted to learn as well so I was happy to work from three in the morning until eight at night. I slept well, actually ate well and thus grew stronger. I also began to understand the soil and the value of all that grows in it.

Having been so unwell for so long had curiously given me something of a head start. During the most recent of my many hospitalizations I had become an avid reader of a magazine called *Health for All*. Far ahead of its time – and doubtless regarded then as crazy by some – it addressed issues of diet and nutrition and advocated occasional fasting. I had nothing to lose so I followed the magazine's advice, took an interest in its ideas about compost (it suggested that all domestic kitchen waste should be saved in a bucket and regularly forked through before being spread over a garden to nourish vegetables), and cleansed my body by carefully regulated fasts. After this 'training' I was better prepared than many others for meagre wartime rations and was self-schooled in the nutritional values of foodstuffs which weren't on the ration. Fish, nettles, herbs, good bread and many vegetables were always there for those who troubled to seek them.

Soon, for the first time in my life, I began to feel healthy sometimes, and to this day I regularly fast for short periods to rid my body of toxins. These days I'm more likely to regulate my daily diet than go on long fasts, but if I do I'll go to a pleasant health hydro or a small villa somewhere warm and take lots of books with me. I'm no puritan and see no virtue in painful self-denial: let the surroundings of a fast at least be comfortable. Upon my return I'll start eating solids very slowly and judiciously, mainly nicely seasoned fruits and vegetables. The principle of the fasting remains the same. The body, especially the colon, is flushed out and cleansed of toxins with masses of pure warm water. At times in the early stages one may feel quite weak and unwell – not surprising when one considers that so much poison is being stirred before it is flushed away – but rewards in strength and energy are enormous and rapid.

Feeling much stronger now, despite what the seven doctors had decreed, and having volunteered to the Ministry of Food before being taken on as a sort of apprentice by that farmer in Surrey, I was on my way. Nearly sixty years have passed and I have never moved away from this little pocket of Surrey countryside. Little by little my wages in those wartime days increased and I was able to save. One of my brothers, Harry, who neither smoked nor drank, sent his army pay to help me. Blanche and I managed to live on my tiny wages and his ten shillings a week!

I know this sounds extraordinary now, especially given that it was a time of national emergency, but within six months I had £20 saved and decided to go it alone. Such is the optimism of youth! I rented a nearby seventeen-acre field for £17 a year and became self-employed. Food production was a priority in Britain during those early war years and I was loaned money by the government to buy potato seed, which enabled me to grow my first crop – five acres of spuds. I hand-planted that seed, one by one. I will never forget the help I received from local farmers who must have been amused, really, by my efforts. But they never mocked me.

I was living in a hut I'd built myself in a corner of my field, and my wife and I survived largely on swede, cheese and nettles, cooking on a camping stove. I worked till I was exhausted and slept like a baby until it was light enough to get up and work again. Eventually further grants enabled me to buy a tractor and a lorry. I'm making it all sound rather carefree and almost romantic but it was hard work.

I was now, however, able to undertake it. Many of the required skills came quite naturally and the ordered simplicity of my life suited me well. I felt at ease with the landscape, the soil, the weather and the things that grew in abundance around me. My produce sold, I scratched a living; I was enjoying life and wanted to expand.

Soon after the war my bank manager advised me to buy some land and offered me a loan. I took his advice and in 1948 I was able to ask some local men to build me a house. That year I also joined the Soil Association. Blanche and I raised our family in that house and it is still my home. I went into the greenhouse business as well as cultivating my own potatoes and market-garden crops. Many people who would never have even considered growing or cultivating their own produce were keen to do so in the late 1940s and my business flourished. As I cultivated and nurtured plants and flowers, I gradually came to recognize and then to understand some of their properties.

By the early 1950s Blanche and I had two daughters, Jenny and Ruth, and a son, Stephen. Our family life was pretty simple and typically marked by the usual things – routines, pleasures, a few disagreements and plenty of cheerfulness. I was even seen as a respected and respectable member of the local business community. People worked for me and I was, and I hope remain, a fair employer. But I was taking an increasing interest in the nutritional powers of plants and vegetables, still going on occasional fasts, reading about the body and its magnetic fields and studying in a way that might have surprised my local Chamber of Commerce friends.

A study of crop rotation – the well-known practice that allows a pasture or meadow to rest and replenish for a season or two before being sown again – was just the beginning. My appetite for more information grew and thanks to *Health for All*, for which I was by now a regular organic gardening contributor, I came to know or at least have direct access to many of the experts in the field. To these thinkers and pioneering spirits in the world of plant power we all owe much. Subsequently I became the gardening correspondent for *Here's Health*, and when it amalgamated with *Health for All* I continued to contribute for sixteen years.

My greenhouse crops, vegetables, herbs and flowers all helped my studies. By now, through friends and colleagues, I had learned something of the power of acupuncture, reflexology and many other ways of healing now widely accepted but then held broadly in contempt. A book called *Touch for Health*, written by John F. Thie, founding Chairman of the International College of Applied Kinesiology, and dealing with musculatory problems, was also inspirational. In any event, my plant-based treatments for Blanche had succeeded when conventional medicine had failed. She responded to them and after years of being virtually bed-ridden was able to move, work, function and enjoy life again at last.

Blanche is a dowser herself but her field of expertise differs from mine in that she has shown, over and over again, extraordinary skill in locating missing pets and other animals. She has even been able to trace and track lost children, at least once almost certainly averting serious injury or saving a life.

In any case, I took heart and confidence from Blanche's improvement. My work with her was largely based on diet and nutrition and after her recovery I was encouraged to wonder what my methods could do for others. Fortunately all this coincided with my hitherto growing business going into something of a decline and my cheerful and philosophical view that I had had a good professional innings and this would give me more time to please myself.

By this time people were flocking to supermarkets, which were then fashionable novelties, to buy their groceries, and today's interest in organic food had yet to burgeon. They bought their clean and neatly wrapped packets of fruit and vegetables rather than my dirty, earthy crops. But I took this in my stride and wrote more, read more, quietly continued to cultivate my organic plants, herbs and flowers, and dowsed rather more as word of my skills spread.

Patients kept coming back and recommended me to their friends. Twenty years ago I had only three patients but now my appointment book is full for weeks or months ahead. I see at least fifty people a week and have had few complaints. Thus I can only assume that my work helps. And if they don't return I might assume that they don't need me any more – which is the best that any healer should hope for. Given that I always tell patients that relief or remission, not cure, is what I aim to achieve, it's pleasing that so many of them *do* keep in touch, even though their particular course of treatment is completed – and so, yes, I do feel pride at the evidence of some of my results.

Couples who had despaired of conceiving have sent me photographs of bonny children born after treatment here in my Surrey clinic. A young woman whose problems with recreational drugs had left her looking and feeling wretched sent me an almost unrecognizable portrait taken after I had removed years of ghastly toxins from her body: not only is she no longer tragically wasted and aged but every other aspect of her life is slipping back into its correct place. A world-famous fashion model, previously stricken with crippling back pain and spinal problems, is now gloriously pain-free and working hard again . . .

Although I can analyse an ailment if a patient calls me from halfway across the world by dowsing a hair clipping or fragment of fingernail already logged in my laboratory, I can never generalize. If you suffer from migraine, backache, a bowel disorder or some nervous stress, I cannot write a quick prescription and hope – like you – for the best. All my treatments are based on understanding the patient's unique DNA and personal aura, as divined by my pendulum and now, sometimes, by the wise stones which stand in a circle outside my practice.

Today many patients ask me if I am in touch with the spirit world since, to them, I seem to know so much. As will become clear in this book, a respect for that world and its powers came to me long after I began working as a healer. I appreciate now that for someone like me, with no recognized medical qualifications, an ability to trace and identify and then deal with physical malfunctions is so great a gift that some other force may be helping me in my work. My answer is thus simple.

I do ask my pendulum if there is someone on the other side who has the knowledge to help me deal with the problems which confront my patient and me. If it says yes then I am delighted to know that I am locked and linked with an expert who will guide me towards the priority area that requires treatment. After that I must work out what the problem is and the treatment needed. I generally ask of my 'helper' when they died and at what age. I also ask them about their nationality. I have found it interesting that so many of my partners from the other side have been French, German, Austrian, Spanish, Danish, Russian or Polish: all

European, you see. No Native Americans or Atlantic people have yet helped me in this way. And recently I have been helped by Swami Muktananda (1908–1982), who was a disciple of Siddha Yoga and who was tremendously influential in promoting the art of yoga in the Western world, so I feel that good and kind spirits are with me.

At first I worked from an upstairs room in the house I built all those years ago. Now my surgery is a single-storey complex built on the same land that used to feed my market garden, but that old house is just across the field.

I find the time to search the world for plants and minerals which will help treat individual patients and my pendulum nearly always guides me in my searches. I might hold it over my atlas or a map and listen to my internal voice as well as watch how it swings. Or I might dowse over the clippings of hair and nail that I keep in distilled alcohol for each patient and ask questions of that little phial, observing the silver stirring or whirling as I ask it to tell me what I need to find and where I should go.

Once I travelled eight hundred miles after arriving in South Africa in search of healing plants. But I don't travel haphazardly, and I try to pinpoint my exact destination, almost to the special copse or garden where I will find my healing remedy, before I leave my home in Surrey, let alone my hotel. Hiring a taxi driver at that end of the quest is not yet something I have dowsed for but it is remarkable how often a local chap has instinctively taken me to within five yards of the very leaf or bloom that I had flown so far to find. This again makes me wonder about the powers of some divine guidance.

Small stones are placed everywhere in the clinic, on carpets, shelves and tables, not randomly, but in places carefully chosen for their energies and powers. Much larger stones, many from Pembrokeshire in Wales, are arranged outside in a circle, interspersed with low wooden benches. Patients who have sat there often remark upon their calming power. Those stones can help to heal, especially where stress-related problems are concerned. Each stone contains the evidence and wisdom of thousands of years, and since I do not believe in accidents I know that I was guided to them whilst on a healing-related seminar that I organized in South Wales only four years ago. I did not seek them: rather they drew me and it is only recently that I have begun to learn and respect their healing powers.

Our forebears understood the universe and its energies and harnessed its power to the betterment of their civilizations. It took many modern scientists aided by computers to realize that a small hole left in one of the Egyptian pyramids was carefully lined up with a special star . . . similarly the neolithic stone circles built by our forebears always had a special purpose. With my dowsing friends I learned how and why the Gors Fawr circles in Wales were built. In our recreation of them we can all tap into the special healing energies their builders understood so long ago.

Some stones are steeped in the sun's energy and others in that of the moon. My pendulum told me that each stone connects with one of sixteen distinct parts of the human body, and very inspiring they have proved to be. My studies of shiatsu, herbalism and all the other alternative sciences are very valuable and are daily enhanced by the nearby wise energy which the stones radiate. But nothing is quite so truthful as the 'yes' and 'no' answers supplied by the swing of the pendulum when I hold it above a rock or a plant and silently ask it a question about a particular patient's problem, pain or fear.

When I first saw HF, who had had an advanced cancer, in 1984, I told her that I could not help until her cells were cleansed and able to absorb oxygen. This I was able to achieve through the use of the mineral magnesium. Although her cancer threatened to return on several occasions she refused the radiotherapy that her hospital advised and came to me instead. She has now been in total remission for some time.

Our bones are indestructible. So are our genes. They control a unique blueprint and I believe that this knowledge is sometimes overlooked or underestimated by the medical establishment. The stones, the plants and the trees can tell us much more about ourselves and our physical and mental needs than any three-minute talk and hastily scrawled prescription from the local health centre. Remember that every hair of your head, every flake of scratched or sunburnt skin, every curl peeled from a nail can speak of the generations long before you and who made you what you are. And so they can help you to recover from whatever troubles you.

We are all within touching distance – almost – of history. It does not take too many generations of ancestors to take us back to the so-called Dark Ages: there weren't many of our forebears alive at that time and reproducing in direct relationship with our own family tree. My grandfather died at the age of 106 in 1929. His father must have seen the Napoleonic army sweep through his part of Poland in 1815. My father was wounded in the leg by Japanese fighters when they invaded Port Arthur, in Manchuria, in 1905. That bullet caused my father great pain and I inherited a subsequent blockage which in turn caused distress in many internal organs. Nothing special about me – such incidents can, and probably have, affected all of us. But my methods of extracting inherited poisons have certainly helped me, as I write these notes some time after my eightieth birthday, and I believe they can help you, too, to escape from unwittingly bestowed legacies from forebears recent or ancient.

If you don't yet believe in the ancient powers that a dowser can release, let me tell you a true story. A few years ago a boy went – with his mother's permission – to buy an ice cream. They were on the sort of wide sunny beach where people often dowse for treasure. Two hours later the mother called my clinic, distraught, and gulped that her son had not returned. Blanche took the call, found a map of the area and dowsed it. Blanche, who did not know that part of the coast, felt sure that the boy was in some marshy place but that he was unable to move because he'd hurt his foot after jumping some ditch. The local police, who had been concerned when informed about the missing boy but unsure as to where to look for him, guessed from Blanche's description where he might be although it was some way from the beach or holiday front where they might well have searched first. They found the child exactly where Blanche's pendulum had suggested they would. He was lying by a ditch with a sprained foot. The boy was rescued and all was well.

Some of my patients have high social profiles. Diana, the late Princess of Wales, came to me when she needed more strength to meet the emotional stresses of her public life and my crystal-based tablets helped her. Diana showed great respect to me and to other patients by insisting, sometimes, that appointments should be rescheduled so that clinic matters would not be disturbed by the press. Her sister-in-law, Sarah, Duchess of York has also been a patient. However, my gratification from the relief of an ordinary mother concerned about her child's well-being and safety, from pensioners who find that they can, after all, continue to enjoy life, or from being instrumental in the change of health and attitude of other patients who play no part in public life, is equally strong.

How can I expect others to have faith in my methods? It took me years to learn them and even today I still hope I have the humility never to assume that I am right. I have much yet to learn, and time for it.

I'm in my early eighties now and feel as strong, if not stronger, than I did decades ago, thanks, I think, to following my own advice. I usually work for twelve hours a day, have a buoyant social life, travel all over the world looking at and for new possibilities that plant and mineral extracts can offer and I don't suffer much jet-lag or fatigue. About the only time I've been ill in recent years was when my stomach was upset after I ate some goat's cheese with a hard rind. The place where that goat had foraged must have fostered plants feeding upon soil to which I proved to be allergic. I was once seriously ill, when I was coral diving in Mauritius. What I didn't know on that holiday was that when I had scratched myself as I touched coral in the West Indies twenty years earlier I developed an allergy to coral. This time I flew back to Britain from Mauritius and was soon in hospital on a life-support drip. I lost a huge amount of weight and feared that it was all over for me, but when I was eventually able to prescribe myself my own medicine – a pad of homeopathic tablets which released a rectum sphincter – I recovered quickly. However, I was so weak that I could only dowse myself by a complex form of blinking (one can actually program eye muscles to blink a prearranged 'no' or 'yes' in answer to silently asked questions that would normally be posed by the pendulum). From the response I got I stopped taking the penicillin that my doctors insisted I needed and was just about able to tell my daughter which of my own remedies I wanted instead. She fetched them for me, helped to apply them and shortly after that I began to recover.

It is not merely a matter of simple faith; but as anyone who has ever crossed their fingers knows, faith and confidence in the healer matter very much.

From rich personal observation and experience I know that dowsing can help and work. I trust the powers of the natural things which surround us and I am both baffled by and proud of my ability to release their powers to heal. In the chapters that follow I want to show how enriching that belief can be.

This book is not just an introduction to my work but a glimpse of the complex and noble sciences that underpin it. In opening it here I have tried to touch upon the range of challenges that I meet in the course of my work every day. Somewhere between the age of the stones and the fresh simplicity of a new green leaf the answers lie, if only we will look at and trust in what we feel and see.

Chapter One

Dowsing

What he does did seem strange at first but he explains
what he's doing including how and why he's dowsing . . .
Some people say it's because I have faith in him that it
works. But when I first went I knew nothing about his
methods, so there was no faith involved . . . I think
basically he's changed everything inside me and now it
all works as it should do. I used to have trouble just going
down to the shops – five minutes' walk took me fifteen
minutes. Now I've got more energy than I know what to
do with. I'm starting to live again.

My patient SJ has been coming to see me for over five years.
She had problems ranging from asthma, 'allergies', weight
loss and excruciating menstrual cramps to headaches and sinusitis.
Many of these were caused by inherited toxins and weaknesses and
from synthetic vaccines. This extract from SJ's testimonial about
my work is typical of many that I receive which show that the
power of dowsing is not merely a matter of my own certainty.

Almost anyone can dowse for almost anything *with* almost
anything. Dowsing has many more applications than is generally
realized, and not only can almost anyone benefit from it, it is a
practical technique that most people, with application, can

master. I want to dispel any idea that it is some form of strangely cloaked sorcery. Its power is mysterious, yes, but so are many things in nature.

However bizarre the idea may once have seemed to businessmen, industrialists and even governments, opinions have changed when dowsing has proved successful in locating potentially disastrous leaks in reservoirs or in searching for lucrative oil beds. In some countries house buyers or builders automatically insist on the dowsing of property or land to ensure that there are no negative energy lines in the soil beneath. Then there are, of course, the beachcombing weekend dowsers who frequently find small treasures and curios as they pursue their harmless hobby. But here in this book we are looking for the greatest treasure of all – that of good health.

I have every confidence that I will live to the age of 140 and be hale until my dying day. Nothing is certain in this world, however, which is why I have a continuous stream of students, like Tony Pagdin – who studied with me for three years and now has his own practice – who can continue and disseminate my methods and ideas. I'm also well aware that it simply isn't always practical – for any number of reasons – for patients to come to me, and so I stress that simple dowsing can be performed at home, either by a friend or on oneself, with a device as basic as a ring looped through a length of string. The essential 'yes' or 'no' response of the swing of the pendulum to silently asked questions is the same in principle in your home as it is in my clinic.

Essentially, I dowse for two purposes: to locate illnesses and to find their remedies. Some people come to me brimming with optimism because of word-of-mouth recommendation, and some come miserably despairing after years of failed conventional medical treatment. Others are somewhere in between. They may be troubled by stress or emotional disorders; they may have some chronic, persistent ache or malaise; they may have some more dramatic and near-unbearable pain; and some might even have been virtually written off by other doctors and effectively advised to sort out their affairs in readiness . . . In short, I see the whole spectrum of patients, from those who have seen a GP to those who have been under the care of senior hospital consultants.

Simplifying the principles of dowsing is not easy. I suppose for some it requires a leap of faith and for others it is eminently logical. Either way, certain elemental essentials must be accepted. In the clips of hair and fingernail that I take from each new patient and store in a tiny phial of alcohol there resides not merely the DNA of my patient but the DNA of every single one of their ancestors, male and female. Further dowsing will tell me which genes come from the female line and which from the male, right side of the body or left. This, in the context of the ailment in question, tells me which side of the family tree I must explore.

By dowsing over that incredible store of information in the patient's phial and employing my usual question and answer technique I learn about hereditary tendencies, ancient strengths and ancient weaknesses. In the blood, bones, muscles, organs and cells of all of us resides the basis of our good health or otherwise today. Even so-called self-inflicted poor health is connected to mindsets which have been passed down, in many different ways, over generations.

By dowsing a patient I can identify a blockage – some essential element of their DNA that has gone missing. And often I can help to restore it. Obviously I've studied anatomy and physiology, so I know where to dowse, and experience has taught me which of my plant or mineral remedies might work best. But it is important to stress that – thanks to the nail fragment and the hair clipping – I am always treating an individual, and what may work fine for one patient may not be quite correct for the next. My pendulum guides me. Each time a unique magnetic force is harnessed, a patient's vibrational field is identified and an answer suggested.

Dowsing can locate the exact area of the body which is causing disease or pain. This can be more complicated, and thus more valuable, than you might suppose. Each human body has the same map of meridians – the invisible lines that link our systems, bones, muscles and organs. Your bladder, for example, is connected to a meridian at the back of your calf: it is here I will dowse if you suffer from a urinary tract problem and here that I tape the correct tablets; a persistent ear infection may be rooted in a disorder far away from that ear. When I have located the source of the problem I can begin to prescribe remedies based on plant and mineral extracts which will begin to help the body to heal itself.

If you are at home and stressed in some way or have a headache but know the maps of your meridians you can put your finger on that line, dowse it with whatever you have at home, silently ask those 'yes' and 'no' questions in order to gradually eliminate and finally identify the source of the problem . . . and then you may be able to treat yourself by stepping up your consumption of correct nutrients. A finger placed on the mid-thigh, which is on the stomach meridian, could either eliminate the headache or, with dowsing, suggest that there is a calcium sulphate or Kali Mur deficiency, the first revealing alkalinity and the latter acidity.

Meridian Lines

Organ	Nutrient
5. Large intestines	Vitamin A Vitamin D Vitamin E Boron
12. Triple warmer	Molybdenum Calcium Iodine Nat Phos Copper Vitamin A Vitamin E
9. Small intestine (Ilium) (Jejunum)	Calc Fluo Kali Mur Molybdenum Uranium
7. Lungs	Vitamin A Vitamin D Calc Phos Calc Sulph Thorium
2. Circulation Sex	Vitamin A Samarian
4. Heart	Chromium Selenium Molybdenum Vitamin E Copper
8. Kidneys	Copper
10. Spleen	Iron
6. Liver	Cobalt B^{12} Iron Kali Sulph
11. Stomach	Calc Sulph Kali Mur
3. Gallbladder	Mag Phos
1. Bladder	Zinc Sulphur Vitamin A Vitamin D Calc Phos Calc Sulph

Use the body's magnetic field for checking nutrient deficiencies.

Using a map of your meridians you can put your finger on the relevant line to find the source of the problem and possibly treat it nutritionally.

CB came to see me after doctors at a London hospital had said that the only way to control her persistent cystitis was the prospect of a lifetime on drugs. She always knew when an attack was imminent because of a pain in her toe – which is on the same meridian as the bladder. I applied the appropriate homeopathic tissue salts (not those in poisonous element form) by means of tablets taped to her toe – natural sulphur, mercury, phosphates and vitamins A and D extracted from plants. Her problem has cleared and she takes no drugs.

CB subsequently brought her niece to see me. She was suffering from such a serious lung condition that doctors had recommended a transplant and said, even then, that she might only have five months to live. I put her on a course of homeopathic tablets made from essential oils of benzoin and pine and applied them to her thumbs, at the tip of the meridian lines which lead back to the lungs. That was more than seven years ago and her respiratory problem, gradually arrested, appears to have disappeared completely.

In each of these instances the pendulum located the source of the problem. By divining the inherited or more recent toxins I was able to prescribe exactly the right fighting natural remedy.

A good example of the effect of dowsing on some relatively new problem is that of my patient LS, whose difficulty in walking I ascribed to poisoning from household bleach. She told me that when she returned home after her consultation, the tablets still taped to her legs, her husband and son both noticed a strong smell of bleach. The tablets were already extracting the bleach poison through the pores of her skin.

Often the first thing I do is to ask patients to open their mouths. It's as good a way to start as any: if they have a mouth full of old-fashioned mercury fillings I advise them to have them removed and replaced by modern porcelain ones. It's an expensive process, but health and life are precious. Impure non-homeopathic mercury is a poison and minute quantities of it seeping into the system are often a major barrier to the body's ability to absorb correct nutrients. I work to rid the body of its toxins so that the essential elements can be free to heal. There are well over a hundred essential elements. The elements working for me have been collected over the years from rocks in five countries and I take my tablets regularly to keep trace elements up to correct levels. The Periodic Table which was given to me nine years ago lists 103 elements; however, after my journeys to Oban, Madeira, the Pyrenees and other places, I dowsed for and collected rocks suitable to crush into flour and turn into absorbable tablets. As I did this the total number of elements gradually rose. I then dowsed where I should go to find the next rock to make up any missing elements, and I was surprised to find that my pendulum findings did not let up until I reached the element level of 130, well above the Periodic Table. I also found it necessary to dowse and match each tablet with a synergist, in other words a herb to enable full absorption to take place. When I go away and do not take my tablets regularly the level of elements in my body gradually falls, and within a period of seven days I lose at least forty elements from my system. I have noticed that my patients taking these tablets containing 130 elements have a power of endurance which is quite remarkable. Just how modern farming methods have robbed our soil of elements that would have been naturally in place only a few decades ago is explored later in the book.

Periodic Table of the Elements

1 H Hydrogen																	2 He Helium
3 Li Lithium	4 Be Beryllium											5 B Boron	6 C Carbon	7 N Nitrogen	8 O Oxygen	9 F Fluorine	10 Ne Neon
11 Na Sodium	12 Mg Magnesium											13 Al Aluminium	14 Si Silicon	15 P Phosphorus	16 S Sulphur	17 Cl Chlorine	18 Ar Argon
19 K Potassium	20 Ca Calcium	21 Sc Scandium	22 Ti Titanium	23 V Vanadium	24 Cr Chromium	25 Mn Manganese	26 Fe Iron	27 Co Cobalt	28 Ni Nickel	29 Cu Copper	30 Zn Zinc	31 Ga Gallium	32 Ge Germanium	33 As Arsenic	34 Se Selenium	35 Br Bromine	36 Kr Krypton
37 Rb Rubidium	38 Sr Strontium	39 Y Yttrium	40 Zr Zirconium	41 Nb Niobium	42 Mo Molybdenum	43 Tc Technetium	44 Ru Ruthenium	45 Rh Rhodium	46 Pd Palladium	47 Ag Silver	48 Cd Cadmium	49 In Indium	50 Sn Tin	51 Sb Antimony	52 Te Tellurium	53 I Iodine	54 Xe Xenon
55 Cs Cesium	56 Ba Barium	57 La Lanthanum	72 Hf Hafnium	73 Ta Tantalum	74 W Tungsten	75 Re Rhenium	76 Os Osmium	77 Ir Iridium	78 Pt Platinum	79 Au Gold	80 Hg Mercury	81 Tl Thallium	82 Pb Lead	83 Bi Bismuth	84 Po Polonium	85 At Astatine	86 Rn Radon
87 Fr Francium	88 Ra Radium	89 Ac Actinium															

58 Ce Cerium	59 Pr Praseodymium	60 Nd Neodymium	61 Pm Promethium	62 Sm Samarium	63 Eu Europium	64 Gd Gadolinium	65 Tb Terbium	66 Dy Dysprosium	67 Ho Holmium	68 Er Erbium	69 Tm Thulium	70 Yb Ytterbium	71 Lu Lutetium
90 Th Thorium	91 Pa Proactactinium	92 U Uranium	93 Np Neptunium	94 Pu Plutonium	95 Am Americium	96 Cm Curium	97 Bk Berkelium	98 Cf Californium	99 Es Einsteinium	100 Fm Fermium	101 Md Mendelevium	102 No Nobelium	103 Lr Lawrencium

The Periodic Table lists 103 elements, but by dowsing I find that the human body can use up to 130 elements, which I have been able to put together from rocks collected in different parts of the world.

Suffice to say here that one and a half tons of wheat was produced for every designated acre in Britain sixty years ago and now it's four tons. Four tons of what?

I'm deeply opposed to the vaccination of babies and children. I accept that for some people an artificial vaccination against a serious illness is better than no treatment at all, but I'm afraid I prefer the natural way, which is often the slower if not actually the harder way! I believe that vaccines, often carried with the same formaldehyde which is used for preserving corpses, place poisons into young bodies which can harm them for life. Some other vaccines are made with aluminium sulphate or non-homeopathic mercury – both of which I believe cause poisonous blockages in the body which prevent the healthy natural fightback. It rather depends on whether a patient chooses to put their trust into one quick shot or is prepared to invest time in a long lifetime of better health. Recognition of this is increasing, with horrific reports in many of our newspapers, but for the afflicted children and their anguished parents this spread of awareness may be too late. I had to go to court to prevent the compulsory vaccination of my three children – now all in blooming middle age. I have no regrets and neither, I think, do they. I believe that a carefully nursed child will recover from measles or whooping cough and become better equipped to cope with adult ailments and stresses than one who has been poisoned by the immunizing needle – but I'm aware that many people would disagree with me. I realize that not everyone will choose the organic route to prolonged health but the protection and preservation of our immune systems is very important and the choice is yours. The body will always take care of itself if its true needs are respected and supplied.

All my treatments are based on using the body's meridians,

and although all my tablets are applied externally, I have to be realistic and sometimes advise the patient to take certain specified nutritional supplements which they can buy at good health food shops. Years ago, when study had led me to my central beliefs, I had no hesitation in 'putting my money where my mouth is' and hiring a skip which I filled with over £2,000 worth of existing non-productive stock. It made a clean break and forced me to start all over again, to find out why nutrients were not being absorbed by the body and its organs. I have stuck to this pathway ever since.

The plant and mineral remedies I now prescribe are all based on things derived from and nurtured by the soil or from stones and rocks – these last are pulverized. I coat tiny innocuous sugar pills with infinitesimal amounts of the appropriate essence, distilled in pure alcohol, and tape them to the correct place on the patient's body. Toxins are then drawn out through the pores of the skin.

Most of the soil in Britain is beyond practical repair. Poor soil can seldom be nourished back into health, even by organic farming, so I have to travel widely to find the leaves, flowers, stones and rocks I need for my work. I might hold my pendulum over an atlas and think 'Shall I go to Goa?' If the pendulum swings and whirls energetically then I know I must. When I get there I will use the same process of question and answer to identify a small region, then perhaps a field or a single tree.

Once, in Luxembourg, where I had gone to dowse in search of a remedy for a lung problem, I had the extraordinary experience of knocking randomly on a front door, being told by the householder that I was expected and that he could help me find what I was looking for. We walked to a forest and up a track. Where it forked he asked me, 'Right or left?' We turned right and at several subsequent forks we took the turn which my pendulum suggested, until we arrived at a clearing where one solitary fir tree stood. It had a luminous quality and on it I eventually found a single pine cone which emitted a tremendously powerful force. I still constantly use homeopathic extracts from this cone to treat lung problems.

Even then the work is painstakingly slow as I might have to dowse scores or even hundreds of individual flowers or trees before my dowser tells me that *this* leaf or *that* bloom has the correct healing force for my work. Even then I will ask the pendulum to tell me, again by process of elimination after a series of 'yes' or 'no' answers, which part of the body may be healed by the properties of that leaf or flower. Then I might ask the pendulum to tell me if my mission is complete. If the answer is 'yes' I will need to gather no further in that spot. But if there is still work to be done – if, for instance, another essence is needed to balance the final tincture – I will continue. Such minute quantities are needed for my work – the healing energies of such special plant cuttings endlessly refreshed in my laboratory at home – that I will probably never need to visit that field or tree again.

On another occasion, travelling in the Far East with a friend, I had an instinct that I would find what I was looking for not in a rural area but in a shop. I told my friend and some time later when we found ourselves in a jeweller's I felt certain that there was a powerful energy emitting from the stock of pearls, which can have a special healing force built up layer by layer. That force encourages the human body to rebuild and heal itself layer by layer, too. I dowsed over hundreds of them without success but suddenly the pendulum began to circle high and fast. *That* particular pearl had the healing field I had been seeking. I brought it home to be pulverized into tablets for treating bladder and urinary tract problems.

We all of us can alter the template, blueprint – call it what you will – of the life expectancy we may have been born with. People born of badly or undernourished parents can overcome that bad start. Once the body has been cleansed of its poisons it becomes receptive to the benefits of an organic diet and tablets I prescribe to match the cause of their suffering. The pearl incident is a good example of my broad philosophy of treating like with like. In many cases I can draw toxins out of a body by placing tablets composed of some natural replica of the internal poison on the correct meridian site.

As I often have to tell patients (and indeed critics), I am not omnipotent and hate to be so regarded. My science – like most science – is educated guesswork and depends to some extent on reciprocal faith. I can't promise miracles and I never do. I can't prevent the damage which someone might sustain from some terrible arbitrary accident in the home, on the road, on the ski slopes or as a victim of a crime. But I can offer an alternative holistic way of dealing with the effects of such misfortunes through my understanding of an individual patient's DNA and my certainty that conventional chemically artificial drugs, anaesthetics, some surgery and other medicines hinder rather than hasten recovery. With an understanding of an individual's DNA and patience rather than faith, perhaps, the body is ready, willing and able to heal itself. How else would our species have survived?

Let me try to clarify. Long before animal or human life there was mineral life and then plant life. It is not for nothing that people talk about the wisdom of the stones and (some of them) consult ancient runes. The very heavy silver pendulum which I often use was made from something quite recently mined but actually created even longer ago than the birth of plant, let alone human, life. Its magnetic field is very ancient, very experienced and very knowing.

Patient HF first came to see me in September 1992 with severe pain all over her lower back and head pain when leaning forward. She told me she was an ex-cancer patient, now in remission after an operation on her uterus in 1984. Her cancer threatened to return on several occasions but she refused the radiotherapy advised by her hospital. I told her I could not help her until her cells where cleansed and able to absorb oxygen. This I was able to achieve using the mineral magnesium. In subsequent years she remained in complete remission and as far as I know this is still the case.

Plants, however, are a different matter, literally. Whilst some ancient societies, such as the Chinese, have respected their properties for thousands of years, in Britain and the West they are normally seen as ephemeral, perhaps decorative things and not much else. Our medieval and herbalist tradition is retained but this represents only a fraction of how plants can help us. And people tend to assume that vegetables bought cleaned and cling-wrapped from the supermarket will be as good as, if not better than, vegetable produce grown organically – and thus 'soiled'. How fundamentally wrong that is.

Almost everything that we eat or drink derives from some soil or other. The meat which many of us eat, remember, is produced by animals which feed on scrub and grass. We are systematically poisoning our bodies if we select foodstuffs which have lost their ancient natural nutrients as a result of chemical 'fertilizers', the exhausted soil utilized in mass production, and artificial preservatives. My theories are connected with what used to be called compost – that dark, damp heap of fruit and vegetable peelings that people often kept in their gardens and spread upon the soil where they cultivated a few potatoes and berries for their own family use. The practice is much less common now but has gained the name of 'organics'.

The whole – holistic – body needs each one of the elements which natural foodstuffs can supply. When even one of the essential elements is missing, an imbalance will be caused. Just one imbalance can cause a 'domino' effect, placing a strain on another part of the body which is working too hard to compensate for the weakness of the first. This overworked body part may well now cease to function properly, and so it can go on until no part of the system is quite whole or well.

Sometimes a non-specific malaise can be as worrying to a patient as an 'officially' recognized medical condition. It took years for the establishment, for instance, to acknowledge that those with ME were truly suffering and not malingering with something they dismissed as 'yuppie flu'. Recently Salford University in England announced that they suspect ME is connected with toxins building up in the system.

CS was lucky when, in 1987, she had a GP who realized that her desperate fatigue and series of 'minor' ailments were related and real, not imagined. She was advised to see a homeopathic doctor. Eventually, a year later, she came to my clinic.

'At that point I could barely get out of bed and downstairs. Sometimes I stayed in bed all day and just got

up to make the dinner in the evening. Then by nine
o'clock I'd be so relieved because it seemed a respectable
time to go to bed again. I couldn't apply pressure to a tin
opener, I couldn't drive, I had to psych up the energy to
keep going for even half an hour. I was leading a
semblance of a normal life.'

I explained to her that recovery would take time –
my treatments don't always work overnight – and she
felt dreadful when I first dowsed to draw out her
toxins. But we persevered. At one point I noticed that
she had coloured her hair and at first she was doubtful
when I told her that chemicals in hair dye can be
harmful. Eventually she was convinced and has used
organic colourants ever since. Other 'innocent' bathroom
things like tampons can create harm, as can the
chemicals used in the manufacture of nylon and other
synthetics which many people wear every day. Just as I
try to draw toxins out of the skin, the dermis can absorb
poisons from outside. I knew that some of her problems
also stemmed from a brief period years ago when she
took the contraceptive pill, and from drugs administered
when she had glandular fever in her teens. Others yet
she had inherited from her heavy-smoker mother's
genes. There was a lot of flushing out to do. But as she
has said:

'It's all under control now. Lots of my friends
are doctors and they all think it's potty. I can see their
faces glazing over when I talk about my treatment.
Dowsing may seem strange but I'd say I was 90 per cent
better now.'

Some of my most gratifying work has been with couples who come to me, sometimes in desperation, because they have tried unsuccessfully to start a family. Others come because of the success I have had with babies and children who were born with seemingly insurmountable disadvantages.

One patient conceived twins just one month after I identified nylon poison in her uterus – four years after she and her husband had hoped to start their family. Another couple, C and LB, brought their baby to me after it was clear that he had no sight. A series of expensive London consultations had brought them scant hope. I could see at once that there was nothing wrong with his eyes and I knew that the problem was neurological and dowsed him accordingly. I was able to unlock the neural pathways of his eyes and extract toxins affecting them and now he has sufficiently clear eyesight that his parents have been assured that he will be able to go to a normal school.

A third couple brought their baby to me after doctors had recommended an operation and then long-term antibiotics to deal with her various fevers, infections and urinary problems. I think they were alarmed when my dowsing identified a brain blockage but also relieved when I said I could help. The urinary infection lifted after dowsing suggested she should be treated with my hibiscus, iodine, radium bromide and a mixture of homeopathic herbs I'd located in Malaysia. Then when the baby began to vomit mucus I was sure that this was gas poisoning which had been inherited in some way. Sure enough, one

of her grandfathers had been gassed during the First World
War. Once again dowsing pointed to the remedy and it
worked. Later I worked to extract the penicillin that she
had been given for a nappy rash. That the baby's mother
could say of me, 'He certainly hasn't got a nice bedside
manner but neither is he intense or sanctimonious. He
isn't charming in any obvious way but he's very alive and
"there". I also feel that if he couldn't help he'd say so,' I take
as something of a compliment.

It is possible to give an accurate reading by dowsing without
actually sitting in front of the patient. In December 1995 I
watched HRH Diana, Princess of Wales, on television. I
recognized she had a problem from the way she held her head and
I dowsed that she was suffering from lead poisoning. I passed this
information on to her sister-in-law, Sarah, Duchess of York.

Within a week or so I received a telephone call from Diana,
asking for an appointment. She wanted to see me, she said,
because my observation of the lead poisoning was 100 per cent
accurate. She told me that, as a schoolgirl, she had pierced her
right cheek with a sharp lead pencil and the point had broken off
into her face. From that time on her left eye had been constantly
swollen and seemed to be incurable. To cover up the swelling she
adopted the pose of holding her head slightly down, which
allowed her hair to cover the eye. Most people thought she was
shy. I then dowsed that her seventh cervical to fourth thoracic
vertebra on her right side was blocked with lead, causing a
blockage in the energy flow to the left side as well as the left eye.
This caused her to suffer from headaches and bouts of depression.
The lead poison caused her neck to be constantly jammed and

painful, and manipulation gave her very little relief from the pain.

I dowsed that she had also inherited lead poisoning from her forebears by their use of drinking glasses made from lead crystal. This therefore set the scene for one of her lifetime afflictions. I dowsed to locate the source of her DNA which I traced to a tree in Crickhowell, South Wales. I used the DNA fragment together with my formula for extracting lead, and over a period of time with this treatment I was able to extract the lead poison; the headaches had gone within seven days of the first extraction treatment.

Around 1989, Diana had injured her right shoulder in an accident and still had debilitating side-effects when I saw her seven years later. I dowsed that the right arm ball joint was out of its socket by a quarter inch, and this had an adverse effect on how well her thyroid functioned. Patients suffering from this problem are always emotional and may burst into tears at the slightest provocation. By balancing each muscle and aligning the vertebrae, I was able to solve the problem. I applied a pad of my special deep bruise homeopathic remedies, gathered especially for this purpose, to encourage rapid recovery. In view of the right socket weakness I also advised Diana not to do any strenuous exercise, such as on a rowing machine, which would have a pulling effect around the ball joint.

Diana carried out her many public duties without anyone being aware that she also had severe pain in her left lower back which drained her energy and made her feel irritable. I dowsed that the presence of a tetanus vaccine in her colon was causing this problem, which was also aggravated by the pain killers she took. Within two weeks of removing the tetanus vaccine I heard from Diana that she was now able to wake up in the morning with renewed energy.

In April 1991 Diana was involved in a car crash which brought back her neck stiffness, as well as continuous headaches, coughing and an inability to swallow. I was able to readjust her neck muscles and remove the trauma, and the amethyst I gave her at this time also helped her mentally and physically. Diana continued to see me until August 1996, by which time she was able to walk with her head up and look at the world with both eyes.

I don't pretend to know how or why dowsing works so often but I just observe – and so do many of my patients – that it does. Just as I trust my pendulum to tell me where to go in search of plants, stones and minerals, I trust its advice concerning each individual patient. Occasionally, and especially if the patient is not on a 100 per cent organic diet, I will prescribe pills to be taken orally as supplements to my external treatments. Perhaps the patient can't get hold of the right foods and the affected body part is effectively being starved of the vitamins and enzymes it needs. On the whole people don't seem to mind having their tablets taped to their skin for a while, even if the 'bandage' is visible.

I don't know if dowsing will ever become 'respectable', even though the British Society of Dowsers has existed since 1910. And I don't think I much care. The results I achieve are far more important to me than acceptance by a medical and scientific establishment which I do not entirely admire. Whatever they may say I *know* that dowsing can lead to the alleviation of suffering and can help people enjoy a longer and healthier lifespan than they had previously believed to be possible – often far beyond even the three score and ten which for centuries people regarded as a 'good innings'. One consultation here can do the trick, as a famous model with back spasms found. With the aid of the pendulum, the plants, the minerals and the stones, everyone and anyone can benefit. Blockages in their unique DNA, previously blighting their lives, can be cleared and the life force released. Obviously it helps if you clear your life and home from such hazards as common household poisons, sold, ironically, in the name of health and hygiene, but belief in your body's own powers of recovery and proper diet are the most important things.

Moulds can be broken, patterns can be realigned. Both my parents and three of my brothers were susceptible to heart disease and died young as a result. Another brother died after a brain tumour struck and we boys, surely, shared most of the same DNA? I was declared uninsurable at the age of fifty given my record of persistent poor health. But I am living proof, after my eightieth birthday, that these genetic blueprints can be altered. There is every reason to be optimistic.

CHAPTER TWO

The Legacy of DNA

Someone browsing along the shelves of labelled tinctures in my office might imagine I was in some sort of exotic catering business. They would see many names familiar from their own larders – ginger, black pepper, saffron, caraway and cloves. Fenugreek, peach, blackberry and bramble essences are there too, but perhaps the most important phials contain tiny chips of wood taken from tree trunks containing human DNA – including my own, dowsed from a fir tree on the Isle of Skye.

In a sense, I suppose, my office and laboratory *are* like a kitchen, the place which at best is at the heart of warmth and well-being of the home, with the woody DNA fragments utterly central to all I achieve there.

The science of genetics has perhaps been best explained by Professor Steve Jones in several books and in his brilliant Reith lectures for the BBC. Its complexities cannot be better or more briefly simplified. Basically, DNA is the main constituent in our chromosomes; it is self-replicating and transmits hereditary characteristics. We all have millions of genes and each of them has a specific task connected to a body part or function. My work depends on the principle that each person's illness or health is rooted in inherited tendencies. If someone experiences a breakdown, physical or emotional, it means that there is a failure or blockage in a specific group of genes, and for any given ailment I dowse to find the historical moment when the genes in that group were in full health. It may have been during the patient's lifetime, in the womb or at the moment of conception, or much earlier, several generations or even far, far back, thousands of years to very ancient ancestors. In such cases I need to dowse for the DNA on both sides of the family.

In my simplistic approach, I allocate the number of genes required to maintain the faulty part of the system in perfect health. I always multiply genes in their groups. Each group consists of genes in multiples of six, therefore if any area is not functioning properly I just increase the basic grouping of six genes in multiples of six, and when I reach the required number the pendulum gives me an immediate response. The alphabet of each gene consists of four amino acid proteins, adenine, thymine, guanine, and cytosine. Each amino acid protein has its own element, manganese, mercuric, graphite, and sulphur. (See the chart on page 43.) So therefore my approach is quite simple. Is the system working? No. What part is not working? How many genes are there that should be servicing that particular part? How many letters in that gene are not operating? What is blocking those letters? When was the block established – was the person born with the block or was it acquired? What caused the blockage? Was it a poison, a disease, a vaccine . . . ? Once these answers have been formulated I am then aware of the problem.

I have learned that the genetic memory of a dead person is preserved in any ground that they lie buried in, however deep. Bark or a fragment of trunk taken from the south-facing side of a tree growing in that earth will release the DNA answer vital for the correction of a problem today. With the distilled tincture I am

Genetical Blueprints

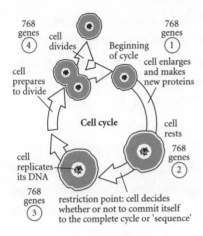

768 genes (4) cell divides

Beginning of cycle

768 genes (1)

cell enlarges and makes new proteins

cell prepares to divide

Cell cycle

cell rests

768 genes (2)

cell replicates its DNA

768 genes (3)

restriction point: cell decides whether or not to commit itself to the complete cycle or 'sequence'

Each gene has a code of 1000 letters controlled by 4 letters in the double helix, each of which are proteins.

Genetical blueprint complete with its own DNA is replicated in the trees from bones buried underneath giving us a complete blueprint of the of the construction of the body.

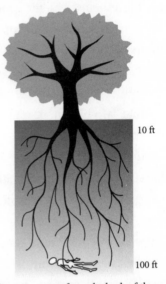

10 ft

100 ft

Adenine [A]
Thymine [T]
Cytosine [C]
Guanine [G]

Tiny squares cut from the bark of these trees contain the genetical blueprint of the skeleton underneath.

They are potentized into homeopathic tablets so that the image of our genetical forebears can be reintroduced back into our systems.

I have generated 120 genetical blueprints which represent millions of people. They were sourced from Marseilles, Israel, the Isle of Skye, the West coast of Ireland, Wales and various parts of the UK.

Nucleotide pairing is always complementary.

Adenine (A) always bonds to **thymine (T)**, and **guanine (G)** always bonds to **cytosine (C)**. Such specific base pairing ensures the precision of DNA replication. The order of the nucleotides on the template strand determines the order on the new strand being built.

able to jump forward, sometimes many generations, and apply the essence to the patient's correct meridian line connected with that particular organ to rectify and clean the gene blockage. The patient's pores will usually absorb the ancient good genes, replacing today's failing ones. The letters are then able to re-establish themselves, the genes can start functioning and the area can start renewing itself, and thus the body is regenerated. Most important of all, we have got to take on board that our cells renew themselves at three billion cells per minute. I then establish what the cell renewal is of the ailing organ – is it three billion per minute, two billion, or one billion – and what is the cause of the decline in cell renewal.

In my own family the men have often suffered from weak hearts and have hair that thinned early – we all inherited faulty genes. Too late for my brothers, sadly, I was able to dowse back four generations and locate the cause of the problem: toxins entering our forebear's systems through a crude black clothing dye that was commonly used, especially in Jewish communities, in the nineteenth century. Taping the appropriate tablets, made from the distilled essence of twenty-one flowers dowsed for on Skye, on the correct body meridian I drew the toxins out and now, I'm told, I have the strong heart of a twenty-year-old. Such is the regenerative power of plants. Moreover my hair, which began to recede in my thirties, is now much more abundant than it was twenty years ago. My fingernails, strong again now, were always breaking or splitting before I dowsed for the fault in the gene pool which influences all these outer and protective parts of the body – hair, skin and nails. My skin tone has improved to the extent that a double chin which threatened to flop further like some turkey gizzard has now retracted and firmed. I think of such cosmetic side-effects as a bonus, however: the real gains have been those of energy and an increased sense of well-being which are merely reflected in my appearance.

People with potential heart problems often experience chills, numbness and pins and needles and so forth in their extremities, even if their blood pressure is registered as normal. Aged fifty, and uninsurable because of dodgy blood pressure, I felt listless most of the time and was always the first to crawl out of the sea after a short swim – frozen and exhausted. This type of weakness also ran in my family. But it's never too late to learn and eventually I realized how I could release my own inherited vascular blockages. But not in time to help my brothers, I regret. We boys all inherited the same collection of weak genes and they might have been helped, like me, by study, faith and dowsing. In another family the problem might have resulted from clay poisoning many generations ago, bronze poisoning or toxins from the soil, usually our friend. In a sometimes slow and laborious process I dowse in the usual 'yes' or 'no' manner to identify the moment when the rot, literally, set in.

I must briefly add here that my belief in the importance of genetic cleansing is worlds away from any deplorable ideas about some master race, Aryan or otherwise: I have no interest in helping to breed any tall blond blue-eyed prototype – or one of any other kind. I just want people everywhere to feel better and to pass on their best to their children.

The fashionable, and expensive, patches which people place on their skin in order to kick a nicotine habit work in much the same way. I was quite pleased at the time of all the furore about these patches to see some vindication of my 'cranky' ways – another case of ancient wisdom was being rediscovered and replicated.

We have been addressing the physical body inherited from our parents via their respective DNAs. This body has to be nourished with produce from the soil from whence we all came and where we will ultimately return. This is why – for the sake of future generations as well as for ourselves – we should all be watchful and live and eat as carefully and organically as possible. Modern toxins can be recognized and avoided – as this book seeks to show – so that new, sad and negative genetic DNA inheritances can be minimized for future generations.

This means a serious reassessment of what you keep in your larder, your bathroom and your wardrobe – 'little' things like non-organic fruit and vegetables, shampoos and air fresheners, antibiotic drugs from the chemist and nylon clothing. Remember that all our rubbish and refuse goes somewhere and that whether it is burned, recycled, dumped in the ocean or in the earth its essential composition does not disappear but is merely modified. I cannot overstress that what is absorbed through our pores, stomach lining or via vaccinations and later released into the planet can have astonishingly far-reaching effects. And not just for us and our immediate descendants but upon anyone who eats foodstuffs cultivated in soil where we may eventually lie, animals that graze on grass there – and the whole ecosystem. Not for nothing is our planet called *Earth*.

What we put next to our skin can be damaging as well as beneficial, the skin being as willing to let toxins in as to release them. If dye colours the water when clothing, sheets or bath towels are washed, don't use them any more. Most commercially produced dyes are toxic. However much you paid for the garment, it was too expensive – throw it out. You can buy a new shirt but not a new body. Some dyes can eventually prove to be deadly.

Remember that if your system has absorbed and learned to tolerate poisons they will be passed down, through your DNA, to your children and to endless future generations until the toxins are removed and the gene pool regenerated. Or until the problem – gradually exacerbated over successively weakening generations – creates truly tragic complications. I do not wish to be alarmist but I must offer some warnings.

Our bodies are genetically programmed to renew themselves, cell by cell, every seven years. If everything is in good running order there is no reason for premature physical decline but an old (or even recent) blip in any group of genes will hinder this renewal process, and I seek to identify then correct those glitches. Poor nourishment is often at the root of problems. The obvious signs of the ageing process – lines and wrinkles, thinning or greying hair, a loss of skin tone or failing eyesight – cannot always be halted but can be slowed down. I'm not calling for eternal life – even the noblest tree must die sometime – but a well-nurtured tree will live for centuries.

Some people may not like the idea of living until they are 135. It will depend on the quality of their life and there is certainly little point in attaining a great age if there is pain or disability. But a corrected genetic blueprint can lead towards a very long, happy and healthy natural life. It's a matter of unblocking the faulty genes and restoring the body to the balance it enjoyed at the moment before a toxin set in and became inheritable.

A person can achieve a great age but not be healthy. It is a mistake to equate long life with good genes: quality of life is what matters. A strong longevity gene cluster may be a curse if other gene groups have failed and cause chronic illness or pain. The kidneys or the heart may struggle on despite a slowing of their renewal rate. Sometimes the body tolerates this and other organs strain to compensate for such weaknesses. But how much better if the complete genetic balance can be restored.

The waxing and waning of the moon also affects our body's efficiency in absorbing salts and other nutrients and the powers within those foodstuffs, as our forebears knew very well when they planted their seeds and harvested crops.

I strongly recommend the use of Schussler Salts, which can be obtained at most good health shops. The calcium, phosphates and magnesium they contain, amongst other things, are easily absorbed by the skin if tipped into the bathwater in specified quantities and will guard against many ailments if there is merely a general malaise and a visit to a dowser is not practical. An unbalanced gene pool can respond miraculously to the use of these salts.

In a way this all connects with another science which interests me – that of astrology. Without going into detail about a complex discipline which is already explained in the books of hundreds of experts and specialists, I would certainly say that everyone will find it beneficial to research and seek out the foodstuffs most relevant and beneficial for those born under their birth sign. As Dr G. Carey, following Dr Schussler's work, pointed out in *Birth Salt Deficiency*, we are all linked at birth to a predominant salt and we tend to use up more of these cell salts as we age – particularly around the time of our birthday – and thus deficiencies can develop. It can only enhance general health if a daily booster of the appropriate one is taken, either in the diet or in a simple form available at health food shops.

Aries	Kali Phos	potassium phosphate
Taurus	Nat Sulph	sodium sulphate
Gemini	Kali Mur	potassium chloride
Cancer	Calc Fluo	calcium fluoride
Leo	Mag Phos	magnesium phospate
Virgo	Kali Sulph	potassium sulphate
Libra	Nat Phos	sodium phospate
Scorpio	Calc Sulph	calcium sulphate
Sagittarius	Silicea	silica
Capricorn	Calc Phos	calcium phosphate
Aquarius	Nat Mur	sodium chloride
Pisces	Ferr Phos	iron phosphate

Conventional medicine recognizes the importance of genetics but often attempts to chemically replicate natural genes. Although this recent respect for the general idea is welcome, I challenge the value of the means, compared to natural methods.

My belief in the importance of correcting any genetic imbalance on both the mother's and father's sides cannot be overstressed. The danger of children succumbing in later life to illnesses that had troubled their parents, grandparents and great-grandparents can now be minimized. The eradication of family tendencies towards certain illnesses is not merely for the young ones of today but for *their* children. I'm pleased to say that in some cases a dangerous genetic blueprint has been reprogrammed.

Some of my patients were having trouble conceiving and I was able to help: I believe my work to be at least partially responsible for the birth of nine beautiful healthy babies and children. Perhaps this is the best work I have ever achieved; I think that the previously despairing parents of those bonny children would agree.

Some couples had been desperate to start their families after years of failed attempts, others were willing to patiently prepare and genetically cleanse before conception, or anxious to have genetic weaknesses fixed during pregnancy. Now they all have children who will not carry into this world an old, flawed genetic blueprint. Many more parents have brought their ailing babies to my clinic and I have been able to treat the infant by extracting inherited toxins and thus steer them towards healthier growth.

One very special couple, Donna and Mark, came to me just as they began to plan their family, and I will happily let Donna speak for herself and to summarize some of my views about the importance of the understanding of genetics.

'We go and see Jack as often as possible so that both our systems can get cleared of our genetic problems so that ultimately our children will have a great beginning in life. What better can one give a child before it is born?'

Donna was constantly tired when she first saw me and I identified a kidney problem, a weakened immune system and a reproductive system adversely affected by the nicotine, alcohol and – occasionally – drugs she had taken as a student. Even if she hadn't been planning to start a family her lassitude would have been worrying.

'I struggled emotionally nearly every day of the week. I'd feel depressed or frightened or unable to motivate myself. I'd feel needy and insecure . . . Once my brain was brought back into balance I could see the world more objectively, as a calmer place. I became less depressed and was really able to start growing up and letting go of all my old childhood trauma. I started to live a normal life . . . '

It wasn't just the physical symptoms that had to be removed to prepare Donna for parenthood. Emotional scars had to be addressed as well as problems in Donna's colon and pain in her hip which made her feel ten years older than she was. Some distorted cells in Donna's right lung also responded to treatment. Her menstrual cramps reduced in intensity – but only gradually – and an arterial blockage causing problems all down the right side of her body was cleared by the application of appropriate tablets after dowsing. Many of these problems stemmed from a genetically inherited bleach poisoning which I was able to remove. Camphor poisoning had attacked her gall bladder and brain functions and this too was removed. Ferrous phosphate was used to correct her iron levels which in turn repaired damage to her liver, spleen and kidneys.

I'm making Donna sound like someone absolutely riddled with illness: she wasn't, but she did have an accumulation of complaints that made her feel physically and mentally unprepared for motherhood as well as concerned about passing damage on to her children. Mark had some problems of his own which I was also able to treat and deal with. I was eventually able to restore Donna's entire reproductive DNA to the optimum condition of her forebears – when everything was perfectly attuned. She looks and feels very well indeed and the pair of them look forward to the birth of a first child with absolutely no inherited genetic disadvantages. You could call it 'good riddance' and Donna should have the last word.
'I'm getting healthier and healthier and my energy levels on a day to day basis have increased enormously. I really am feeling fabulously alive. It's wonderful.'

CHAPTER THREE

Healing the Past, Present and Future

Everyone loves mysteries and yet, perversely, it is human to seek to untangle them and thus render the mystery mundane.

Looking at and interpreting patients' auras, now so central to my work, is still something of a mystery to me even after some years of study, so each discovery remains exciting. And the knowledge that this aspect of my healing yields such enlightenment and subsequent success is more exciting still.

The word 'aura' means different things to different people – a gentle breeze or zephyr, an emanation from flowers, a discharge of electricity, cold air rising from some part of the body . . . An Oxford dictionary definition is 'a distinctive atmosphere diffused by or attending a person', and we often read or hear about people who are said to exude an aura of power, glamour, confidence, sex appeal or evil. For some people this *is* what auras are about. In holistic medicine the aura is usually seen as the combined energies of the various parts of a human being. Sometimes these parts are described as 'bodies' including spirit and matter, the logical mind, the emotions, the soul and the physical body. All these make some sense to me and this chapter concerns my personal understanding of our auras and what they can tell us.

My definition concerns a different sort of magnetism which

relates more generally to physical function rather than to emotional or manipulative ability.

Some years ago a technique (later known as Kirlian photography) was developed in the Soviet Union and this undoubtedly gave scientific credence to the notion of the human aura. Kirlian photography showed emanating waves of differing shape and colour radiating from the human form. Just how these patterns were analysed depended on the agenda of the particular scientist, biologist or psychologist who was 'reading' them. But above all it was absolutely proved that the body sends out startlingly individual signals invisible to the naked eye. Some might be as simple as a register of body heat or stress levels, but other auras tell much more complicated stories about health and ill health and these are the ones which interest me most. For me the study of a patient's aura, in tandem with dowsing, has proved to be an astonishing means of investigating ailments and their roots.

Within us we all carry the rings of many forebears. Each one of us inherits many scores of them. Most connect to people who died between 48,000 years ago and as recently as the earliest years of our century. It may surprise you to learn that sometimes I have deduced from a patient's aura that their health is being affected by a forebear who lived and died not only thousands of years ago – but on another planet. These life forces can be anywhere between 45,000 and 96,000 years old. And it may astonish you even further to read that I have helped patients to 'cheat destiny' by seeing in their aura an inherited illness that was not destined to strike for many years and of which there are not yet any discernible symptoms. These I call Quantum Leaps (although I realize that other people use the phrase in a different way), and the auras relate to people who will die sometime within the next 18–141 years. Yet auras need not be the genetic legacies of ancestors. You may have acquired the genetic aura simply by eating fruit from a tree flourishing in soil nourished by the remains of someone who died far away and long ago.

Crucially, however, I believe that our well-being is also affected by hundreds of spirits with whom we have no genetic connection but which have somehow flown into us. The forces within our auras come from about two hundred other departed souls. Many will have been healthy and altogether balanced people and their auras bestow strengths. But others may have suffered a particular trauma or disease at the time of their death and this will imbue the aura they leave behind with a specific weakness or negativity.

Each ring will have a specific influence on a particular area of our body and each person's complete magnetic aura is unique. Therein we may espy the strengths and weaknesses of our genetic inheritance – I have no difficulty today in identifying the incarnation or the faults connected with it. This seems to me to be such a logical extension of my study of the soil, and holistics, and my belief that something of the past resides in all of today, and the future too, that what once seemed like a breakthrough to me now seems only natural.

In a living person's aura today will be reflected the same part of a system which was flawed at the time of a previous incarnation's death, and the aura will drag from the living system a vital tissue salt, mineral, vitamin or protein so that there will always be a deficiency in certain essential nutrients. This in turn means that my patient today may be destined to suffer problems akin to those of this previous incarnation. Through dowsing I can tell whether a flawed aura comes from a reincarnation, from someone yet to die (or even be born), or from life on any one of five planets. In every case there is the same kind of magnetic drag on the resources of today's physical body and the closer, in age, we get to the time of the incarnation's death the greater is the deficiency in our own physical body. After that age the problem will worsen. But I can set about averting this and correcting a defective aura.

In these instances I do not adhere to the maxim of 'if it ain't broke, don't fix it'. As I see it, this is 'prevention is better than cure' taken to the most dramatic of extremes. For sometimes we *can* anticipate breakdown and I regard it as part of my duty to try to staunch wounds yet to happen – call it damage limitation if you will, or cutting it off at the pass. It amounts to the same thing.

Auras move at their own speed and in their own time and from place to place. And just as pain is our friend, alerting us to a problem, so are our auras largely benign. What makes each of us so fascinatingly unpredictable is the fragments of aura that our genes have collected over the centuries, some more dominant than others, and we all, in our turn, will pass on the auras (and perhaps a few new ones of our own), if we have children ourselves. And it is in this area that my work differs perhaps most sharply with that of other practitioners who ignore the importance of spiritual influence over the physical body.

Without actually *seeing* it I can measure the extremities of a patient's magnetic aura with the palm of my hand and my pendulum. The aura of an exceptionally healthy person can reach out up to twelve feet but six feet or so is average. Measuring a magnetic aura is not difficult – anyone can do it at home. If you hold a pendulum and walk backwards away from a wall your aura will bounce off the wall and the pendulum will swing until you have stepped out of the aura's field. It will begin to move again if you now walk towards the wall. However, since in even the healthiest of people auras of different strengths are emitted from different parts of the body, this bouncing method does not help much in locating an aura weakness. With patients I use my hand to ascertain precise areas of zero energy which indicate a defect in an acquired aura.

I can now remove a blockage in a patient's aura by putting tablets related to the illness onto a small silver plate about two and a half inches square, which is hung over the patient's chest with correcting formulae, each one accurately dowsed for, taped or fastened to the outer surface. This plate rests on my patient's body until the relevant aura is cleansed of its inherited defects, but the effects can be instant with the magnetic pull of the aura weakened and finally broken. Now the patient's body can utilize essential nutrients and the distressed area will gradually acquire normal health.

Knowledge of elements, vitamins, tissue salts, proteins, essential fatty acids and solid fat is essential when approaching an aura-based problem. Each defect in an aura prevents the body from absorbing two nutrients, one of which will be an essential element. For example, anyone unable to absorb gold will be prone to depression. If that person can't absorb vitamin C in addition, they will also suffer badly from colds and the like.

Modern, but in my view unenlightened, methods of approaching illness with the surgeon's knife or synthetic chemicals don't work, because the problem is being approached from the wrong angles. Healing is much more to do with lifting pain and blockage and restoring physical balance by cleansing the aura than with hacking away at damaged parts or absorption of distorting drugs. With my dowser responding with a 'yes' or a 'no' to the questions I put to it, my observation of countless patients' responses and the results that are achieved once the aura slate is cleared so that correct diet and supplements can take over the completion of repair, I have ever greater faith in my own methods.

A highly educated patient told me that there is no such thing as time or space – that past, present and future are all one. This reinforced my own Quantum Leap theory and belief that we can circumvent illness otherwise set to strike in the future. An aura can travel freely through time and space bestowing ghosts of element or tissue salt deficiencies which can affect anything – for good as well as ill, I must stress – from bone strength to eyesight, from fertility to respiratory power. These days when I make a preliminary examination and early dowse, I always ask the pendulum if this patient's problem is connected to the past or to the future. If a problem is lurking, waiting to happen, I will gauge the age of the dead person whose aura surrounds my patient when the problem struck *them* and I will take appropriate evasive action. Sometimes auras warn me of trouble yet to strike . . .

A seven-year-old girl was brought to me with curvature of the spine. A hospital specialist had already offered her parents the options of surgery or a very lengthy period of encasement in plaster for their daughter. Neither appealed. After giving the child the appropriate remedy on the silver plate her spine corrected and straightened itself as we watched. However astonished the girl and her parents were, this was not magic: I had identified in her aura an incarnation of some unfortunate future child destined to die with spine-related trauma.

One thirty-two-year-old patient had a heart problem causing inhibited blood flow and there was a tremendous

build-up of toxins in his bloodstream. In dowsing I found
that his problem lay in pro-incarnation – that the aura of
someone who would die in seventy-one years' time, aged
thirty-one, was affecting my patient. This pro-incarnation
was cutting off my patient's absorption of iron phosphate
and the vital element cadmium which fights toxin build-
up in a system. I was able to help him by addressing the
future aura and his heart started to function normally at
once. His bloodstream was soon clear of toxins too.

Another patient, aged seventy-five, had severe pain right
across his lumbar region. His aura was damaged and
influenced by someone who would die ninety-three years in
the future, at the age of seventy-one. That aura was cutting
off his physical body's ability to absorb carbon and calcium
fluoride – both vital for the health and strength of bones.
I was able to mend his aura. Yet another patient, who was
seventy-three, had a fault in his aura caused by someone
due to die in twenty-one years' time, aged seventy-four.
This time a faulty aura was attacking my patient's liver and
causing deficiencies in vitamin B_{12} and cobalt, both
necessary for healthy liver function. Again I was able to help
him by cleansing the aura of this pro-incarnation.

I can assess a person's aura in about thirty seconds using the palm
of my hand and a pendulum. Sometimes I feel a coldness, which
means the aura is absent or weak or that there has been a break in
the patient's magnetic field for some reason. If so, I am not unduly
dismayed because auras can be reflated or even recaptured. Once
a faulty aura has been repaired and is no longer projecting illness

inwards, the body is fitter to heal itself or respond to my help. Of course I aim to see 100 per cent of the patient's aura, but I can make do with as little as 40 per cent if it is elusive or weak.

I was only able to locate and identify 60 per cent of the aura of one patient – a young woman who first visited me fifteen years ago. In the intervening years she had succumbed to surgery more than once and several essential 'wires' had been thus cauterized, crippling her aura. I have tried to jump-start them but with so much essential aura now damaged or removed I can hold out little hope for full recovery, alas.

I am pleased that individuals are all unique; sometimes I think it would make my work faster and easier if there was a blueprint, standard remedy for every set of similar symptoms, but I try not to generalize. I do promise to treat each of my patients with respect for the individual that they are and to tailor my treatments to *their* unique needs. To accomplish this I must be open to every new possibility of steering a patient back to the full potential of their holistic health, combining dowsing with old wisdom and new learning. Doubts and a negative attitude can also affect the success of my work but I try to remember how hard it must often be for weakened and exhausted patients to muster enthusiasm and faith for treatments which some acquaintances might have been cynical about. Here it is part of my job to establish trust and sometimes an explanation of how my work connects with more established ideas – such as the widely accepted precepts of the body's yin and yang. Even reminding patients that a well-known homeopathic chemist has enjoyed royal patronage for decades sometimes helps. But in any case I will only give patients treatments which they need or feel comfortable with. And although my consultations are for a basic forty-five minutes I will stop much sooner if the patient requests it. Equally I may continue working with them for two hours if progress is too good to be interrupted.

I know now that it is almost always essential to dowse a patient's aura in a very early stage of their treatment. It was after hearing the Dalai Lama speak about reincarnation and the souls within our magnetic auras that I began to take a greater interest in the whole field. Patients of every age and with almost every imaginable problem – physical or emotional – can be dowsed with even greater precision and accuracy than before now that I have a glimmering of their aura's power and spirit force.

Each one of us has a personal DNA aura covering the whole of our skin system. This aura is a network of sensors emanating from the spine, linked to the brain and radiating all over the body, sometimes known as dermatomes. Also located in the spine and connected by the spinal cord to the brain are our systems' nerves and their messages upwards keep the brain informed about the state of things throughout the body.

Until recently it had not been appreciated that in babies this vital information network can be so blocked and damaged by something as apparently harmless as the application of a petroleum-based skin salve that the dermatomes cannot function.

Thirty-nine-year-old VH had suffered for as long as he could remember with respiratory problems and severe headaches brought on by chronic sinusitis. Many hospital consultations, including a cat (CT) scan, had failed to locate the source of the trouble so none of his treatments had helped.

Dowsing of his forehead revealed that within an hour of his birth his forehead had been smeared with a petroleum-based cream and from then on his dermatomes had been unable to communicate with his spine. My dowsing of his forehead registered zero magnetic activity in the area and bacteria thrive in such places. In VH's case it was also cutting off his supply of natural vitamin C and the element thorium which our systems need to produce mucus. This accounted for the entire sinus area drying out and thus the sinusitis.

I applied a pad of homeopathic tablets made from petroleum cream (in accordance with my practice of treating like with like), thorium, vitamin C, some of my Circle Energy remedy and a solution which I call Phagus 587 which contains a genetic memory of bygone diseases. Within an hour his current headache had lifted and his breathing had become normal. When I measured the magnetic network of the area I found that this, too, registered a normal level. VH's sinuses have remained clear and his headaches have stopped.

Time and time again I have noticed that people who were treated as newborns with petroleum products suffer blockages and poor cell renewal around the area of the body where the cream or salve was applied. VH's relatively simple case history is just one of many instances where an understanding of the body's aura has helped me to heal. The study which led to that understanding has been lengthy and demanding, so complex is the whole issue.

Experiment, common sense and faith have helped as much as scientific knowledge.

Other patients whose troubles were rooted in misguided babyhood remedies or inherited conditions which interfere with their auras are often helped very quickly now that I know how much our auras affect our health.

Sixty-year-old SI had severe tinnitus, especially in her left ear, and she was beginning to suffer alarming bouts of deafness. I dowsed the skull around her ears and found considerable loss of bone density and no energy in her aura–dermatome system. Her problem proved to be genetic – deriving from smallpox vaccines given to both her parents before she was born. I had her gene memories and treated the right ear area first, using a pad especially prepared for her. Her hearing returned in thirty minutes and she reported that her head felt generally lighter and clearer.

ST was only thirty-three but had begun to suffer from sciatic nerve pain which her osteopath had not found to be linked with problems in the spine. But after dowsing her left buttock I found a large area without magnetic aura activity. The blockage was caused by zinc and castor oil ointment smeared on her after her birth and was rapidly cleared, as was her sciatic pain.

Zinc and castor oil applied at birth were also the culprits in KS's case. They had affected the meridian lines of the kidneys, liver and spleen, which accounted for her depleted energy. Once again I was able to lift that blockage and all affected organs began working with dramatically enhanced efficiency at once.

All these instances relate to the skin aura. More complex aspects of aura may be less simple to grasp. But now that I have studied the auras of over 350 patients I have seen the emergence of a general pattern.

One female patient, aged thirty-five, had allergies, extreme fatigue and weight problems which I ascribed to faulty auras. She has needed more than one treatment but I have now successfully banished many of her allergies which derived from someone who died, aged twenty-three, 5,678 years ago. For her the formula was a mixture of molybdenum, Kali Mur, Brazilian rock crystal and my Disease Memory formula 582.

Another young woman, GW, was far more exhausted and stressed than she should have been, even with four young children to care for. She also had chest and heart pains. I identified a fault in an aura inherited from someone from another planet who had died from heart and trachea wounds 92,467 years ago. She had a chromium deficiency, and poor protein assimilation was countered by the application on the silver plate of chromium, protein, spalerite crystal and my Accident formula 576. Within an hour her chest felt normal and her heart had calmed completely.

For some people the idea of the quantum leap may be even harder to grasp than the concept of being in possession of auras from ancient life on other planets.

ST, aged thirty-three, has reason to accept it. Until I treated her, bowel problems had prevented her from enjoying work and she felt generally depressed and sluggish. I realized that one of her aura rings was coming from a twenty-two-year-old who was destined to die from a bowel disease in nineteen years' time. After I had fixed cobalt, kurdi rock, vitamin D and Disease Memory formula 582 to the silver plate the faulty aura was broken and her life transformed.

OR was super-fit at forty until she developed bone pains in the lower half of her body, especially around her hips and feet. In dowsing I found that she had the aura of someone due to die from a bone disease in about thirty years. This aura fault was draining her of carbon and calcium fluoride. After I applied carbon, calcium, basalt and Disease Memory formula 582 her pains diminished within the hour.

Respecting the spirit force is another aspect of my work with auras. It is given to us by a higher power and given back to that power when we die. It is located in all of us about two inches below the V of our collarbone and I have noticed that if there seems to be no communication between the spirit force and the universe the patient will be spiritually adrift and their treatment is harder. The patient may, quite simply, doubt if there is a reason to be alive on earth and is thus less receptive to life-enhancing treatments. In these instances I always dowse energy levels at the sternum as well as adjoining areas like the oesophagus, trachea and thymus in the hope of releasing trapped or latent energies and strength.

With patients like this I often apply to the V of their throats tablets made from soil at the exact centre of the seven-pathway labyrinth I constructed in my clinic's grounds. A wonderful connecting energy will usually radiate.

Any patient's magnetic energies and spirit forces – both of which are linked to a universal dynamo which links us all – will be released by the interaction between the silver plate and the tablets I tape to it. Portable phones etc. must remain switched off for the duration to minimize interference to electromagnetic fields. If I can identify a problem within the patient's aura and correct the balance I can often go on to treat the inner systems by more effective dowsing and corrective homeopathic tablets.

A four-year-old boy, AR, was brought to me in 1996. His parents were increasingly alarmed by his stomach aches and the warts that were spreading all over his body, particularly around the genitals, the groin and on the back of his legs. In his case it was relatively simple to trace his aura to his infant vaccinations and to the contraceptive pills his mother had used before her pregnancy. (Without being in the least self-satisfied at seeing some of my 'crack-pot' ideas gaining respectability, I have noticed recently that some of Britain's most eminent journals and newspapers have joined in the clarion alarm call about vaccinating babies against measles, mumps and rubella.) After his first treatment at my clinic his stomach pains vanished.

Several treatments later the warts had disappeared and Robert seemed altogether happier and was lively and sleeping well. A rather unpleasant and smelly urine discharge had gone also. He has a tendency to sprout moles as well and we shall see if this is now arrested. All this has taken several months and several visits to achieve, perhaps because, in one so young, I worked hard to ensure that the problems in his aura really were derived from his mother – and I do not like to take what might appear to be an easy short cut.

I have yet to meet with failure with these methods. Auras have sent me all over the British Isles and to places far beyond for exactly the plant, flower or stone that I need to convert into tablet form for treatments, but these have never been fool's errands and relief for the patient has been effected much more quickly than it would have been without the wisdom of the old, residual auras of past lives.

When I first began to correct auras I found that it was vital for the patient to have an inner healing force. Because the force needed to correct faulty auras has to be stronger than that which most people are able to produce without help, I dowse in the hope that I can strengthen that inner force. Seating a patient on a very 'high tech' chair which vibrates as I work has made a great, positive difference as I work to correct flawed auras.

Firstly I measure the patient's healing force. If it is 100 per cent they recline in the chair and I place the silver plate, with tablets taped upon it, just below the collarbone. Invariably the healing energy level drops immediately to zero. I then remove the plate and switch on the vibration mechanism and the chair now emanates a firm vibration force. This is not uncomfortable for the patient. The force agitates the bone marrow in which is stored much of the patient's inherent healing power and encourages it to circulate. When the level has picked up to 100 per cent again I switch off the mechanism and replace the silver plate. The body is now able to absorb more of the healing force contained in the tablets. This process is repeated five or six times until the patient's own forces have stabilized at 100 per cent and the remedies are working well to clean up the aura. It takes about an hour for each aura to be completely cleansed and the system to be restored to normal.

What I find most astonishing thing about this development in my work is that the auras can so often *predict* a problem that has yet to manifest itself physically. If a patient has part of the aura of someone who fell ill when they were fifty (and the patient is now only forty-two and seeing me, probably, about some seemingly totally unrelated unease), I can dowse and treat away an illness that has yet to become manifest. This is not tinkering with destiny in some messianic way – but simply another example of how our beings, at every moment of our lives, contain elements of past, present and future.

One of my patients was forty-seven years old when she came to see me after decades of respiratory problems. I applied the silver plate and the compounded crystal tablets that I taped to it were derived from a topaz crystal. Her breathing was strained because she couldn't use the central area of her lungs. Every breath had to be dragged painfully up through that central blockage. In dowsing her aura I found that she had inherited miasmas – or a

predisposition to certain specific diseases – from someone
who had died two hundred years earlier at the age of
eighteen, after tuberculosis.

She was astonished and told me that she had always
felt an affinity towards the late eighteenth century and felt
'at home' in its history. She was even more surprised when
I told her about the topaz, as deep glowing yellows are her
favourite shades for flowers, clothes, interiors and
landscapes.

By dowsing I was able to remove her TB miasmas
along with toxins and steroids more recently acquired in
her attempts to have her lung problems treated
conventionally. She is now breathing normally for the
first time in her life. Of her ten previous incarnations
nine had been pretty healthy. I simply had to dowse back
to the time when her DNA had been functioning
correctly – before the death of the eighteen-year-old who
died in 1785.

Another of my Dutch patients came to me desperately
worried about a range of painful and unsightly skin
problems. I dowsed and found that his aura included that
of a four-year-old child who had died only decades ago as
a result of tulip poisoning. During the Second World War
many people in the Netherlands, starving, resorted to
eating tulip bulbs. I suppose many bulbs do have a passing
resemblance to the nutritious and largely harmless onion,
and I always bear this in mind when seeing a Dutch
patient for the first time. His personal crystal proved to be
derived from turquoise and by extraordinary coincidence

I found that the other, conducting, part of the tablet remedy to be laid on the silver plate was something I had searched for long ago, found in Malaysia and almost casually christened 'tulip seed' because the seeds I found at the heart of a rare and exotic plant had a shape resembling a tulip flower. It all seemed to connect with my belief that healing is often to do with placing like against like. Eric's painful and ugly rashes went away after a very few treatments with tablets suggested by dowsing him and some effective homeopathic treatment.

Most of you will be familiar with the expression *Physician, heal thyself*, so it is only right that I should explain how my own self-treatment has given me faith in my ability to help others.

I know that my DNA can be traced and tracked back for 97,000 years but that doesn't mean that my body has been in a constant and continuous state of reincarnation. Centuries can pass between existences – of which I have had 120. Before this current one my last incarnation ended 110 years ago. After considerable research, I don't think we carry auras from our own past lives.

Through dowsing I know that the previous ninety-nine lives were healthy ones but that the twenty-first incarnation suffered from bowel problems and may well have died from dysentery. Since my early life was blighted by bowel and colon problems – now corrected – this makes perfect sense to me. I had to dowse further back to an earlier time and to another ancestor who was free of such problems and treat myself accordingly in order to return to the point when my inherited DNA was in proper balance.

My attitude towards reincarnation differs somewhat from some popular accounts of past lives. We all inherit some of the auras and reincarnations of ancestors – these auras affect our health today as surely as does the visible bruise, breakage, rash or fever. But we don't necessarily inherit the character or social rank of these ancestors. I'm sure you've noticed that many people claim their lineage from Joan of Arc, some Egyptian ruler or Napoleon. Strangely it is seldom an ordinary peasant coppicer, unknown caveman or a shopkeeper who has supplied the DNA pivotal to reincarnation.

Certain unshakeable beliefs underpin all my work.

Our bodies are made up from earthly matter, and when we die we return to the earth to be recycled just as trees, plants, insects and animals are recycled back into the soil to nourish and fertilize new growth. I see little difference with the ashes of the cremated: the Book of Common Prayer speaks of *Ashes to ashes, dust to dust*, after all. I am convinced that our personal DNA is within us and goes with us – I have traced hundreds of individual DNAs from the trunks of trees alone and as I have shown, if a patient has been born with a faulty or incomplete DNA blueprint I can often restore balance by applying DNA from such sources. For although each of us is unique our individual DNA is composed of much more than our genetic inheritance – which is where auras come in.

Next, I believe in that spirit force resting just beneath the V of the collarbone under our throat. When we die that force returns to our God, whoever and wherever He or She may be. I never attempt to harness or tamper with this spirit force – even if I wanted to it would be realms beyond my reach, and rightly so. Conventional doctors, however diligently they may seek the source of a patient's problem, will not locate it because they can address only the physical body and not the invisible aura surrounding it.

I believe there is a vital link between all this which has a profound bearing on our health. In fact, with counselling (often from a colleague here at the clinic) and general guidance many patients have passed through my hands and regained health and vitality merely by rediscovering that link.

CHAPTER FOUR

All Our Lives

So important is the study and use of auras in my work, yet so complex is the science, that here I want briefly to show a little more of the practical scope of my work with auras, its diversity and breadth. Each patient mentioned is real but some have requested that I abbreviate their names.

I have recently seen two young men with very different problems but an iron deficiency was at the root of each. BP, normally as boisterous and lively as any other sixteen-year-old, was lethargic and having such difficulty concentrating that he was lagging behind in vital studies. In his aura I saw the death of a nineteen-year-old 110 years ago and a head injury which had prevented the skull from absorbing iron. I suspected that there might be an attendant carbon deficiency which could lead to lessening of density in the ears' ossile bones and thus to hearing problems. Peter admitted that already he needed to play his music more loudly than before. This incipient hearing difficulty was not improving his schoolwork either. After application of the correct iron- and carbon-based tablets the boy seemed, and remains, very much more alert.

Another young man, CE, who was only eleven, also

had learning difficulties which neither his teachers nor hospital specialists had been able to explain or treat. His aura was blocked by the death of someone who had died at the age of thirteen and he too had an iron deficiency. I was able to treat CE so successfully that schoolwork is no longer such a struggle for him (thus removing much of the classroom stigma that some unfortunate children with learning difficulties are forced to endure). I believe that the sad legacy of that thirteen-year-old ghostly ancestor has now been laid to rest, unable to cause more trouble or damage.

We tamper with or, worse, attempt to conquer nature at our peril – whether that which is natural in the soil, rocks, plants or the invisible manifestations like auras. But we, too, are part of nature and if man can work in holistic harmony and even partnership with nature there is much to be achieved.

To meet EA, a twenty-six-year-old Welshman, for the first time, you might easily imagine that his slow speech and hesitant manner announced some mental retardation, and his life may well have been blighted up till now by such first impressions. His problems certainly weren't eased by some cruel assumptions – also often endured by people with back trouble – that he was malingering if not simple. In fact there is nothing wrong with his brain, but severe blockages internally and within his aura have affected every aspect of his potential since he was about ten years old.

Apart from the outward signs he has symptoms of inappropriate sweating, stiff joints, shaking limbs, lower

back pain and gassy intestines. When I first saw him and
dowsed I could see that his brain had been affected when,
as a child, his head was treated for nits with Carbaryl –
a treatment once common but now withdrawn. Vital
magnesium had been extracted from his nervous system
and thus he could not absorb copper or essential fatty
acids. I applied regenerative homeopathic tablets derived
from the energy I harvest from the ground in which my
stone circle stands and hoped that they would serve to
correct his intestines as well by reactivating the bile system
connected to his gall bladder. The tablets were taped on
his spine – upon the meridian which connects with the
top of his head. Interestingly, when I dowsed his spine for
aura there I could get no reading, so there was blockage in
this area too.

When I next saw EA I asked him closely about
progress and he said that he'd noticed a broad
improvement in things for about two weeks but that this
had not lasted. It was time to test his aura. That he was
prepared to make the long journey to see me again after
the only limited success of his first visit to my clinic speaks
less loudly of me than of the inability of a series of
doctors, both NHS and private, to help him in the past.

The silver plate was affixed and I dowsed the aura –
one hand in front of his head and the other holding a
pendulum behind. For a while I got zero readings,
indicating a gap in the aura which I judged to be about
seven years old. He told me that when he was about
nineteen his troubles had worsened when he came into
contact with sheep dip in Wales. This would have

destroyed an important element called erbium which in turn diminishes absorption of magnesium phosphates and further damaged his nervous system. His problems – which now include a fear of heights – reside within his body but are caused by deficiencies in at least one of his auras and this is what we must address together. I will dowse and examine and treat each one until all blockages are cleared and the problems are eliminated. This will, of course, involve me seeking weaknesses in the auras that he was born with. In an area with low or zero aura energy poisons will accumulate. Ironically, some people lucky enough to have high energy levels and healthy auras would not have been beset with his troubles.

FN had wanted to have children since she was fifteen. Twenty-two years later, and apparently in perfect health, she was still trying. By dowsing I discovered that her womb had been damaged by a reincarnation dating back over 5,000 years when an ancient ancestor had died at the age of twenty-nine from a uterine illness. This meant that her womb had been programmed to struggle to absorb plumbum and magnesium phosphate. Her forebear had died with a trauma which cut off the folic acid vital for fertility.

In all her efforts to conceive FN was thus dragged down by the lack of three essential elements. She had tried distressing and expensive IVF treatments to no avail and after her doctors despaired, she came to me. I treated her with the silver plate and sessions on the vibrating chair to activate internal corrective powers. She began to absorb plumbum, magnesium phosphate and folic acid and in due course I assessed her levels to be normal. I look forward to hearing of a successful pregnancy before long ...

I had been trying to help another woman, TJ, for ten years. She had womb-related troubles as well, with erratic periods, alarming abdominal swelling and fibroids.
I hadn't got very far until I began to study auras and realized that the trouble was not rooted in her physical body. It proved that her aura was damaged by someone who died over 93,000 years ago at the age of thirty-one. This incarnation had lived on another planet – an idea which some may mock, I realize, but one which I hope one day to understand well enough to explain. Her legacy had been to leave TJ with a uterus trauma and iron and para-aminobenzoic acid (PABA) deficiencies which I could correct.

Very recently a forty-seven-year-old patient, EE, came to me almost crippled by rheumatoid arthritis of the fingers, hands, elbows and ankles. She was very stiff, particularly in the mornings, and her swollen hands had only the strength of a jelly. In her aura I discovered that the reincarnation of someone who had died 4,759 years ago, aged forty-two, was robbing her physical body of zinc and sodium sulphate. One session with the silver plate and six weeks later the change in EE and her mobility was truly remarkable. Other reincarnation faults have yet to be corrected but as far as her arthritis is concerned it may be – literally – a thing of the past.

CT, aged forty-one, was depressed, exhausted and almost beyond coping with life. As a professional violinist, leading a string quartet which gives concerts all over the world, she was not only worried about letting herself down, but failing her fellow-musicians and the public. Previous treatments had helped at first but the beneficial effects never lasted. I found that she was suffering from a zinc and vitamin D deficiency inherited from the aura of a thirty-six-year-old who died over 3,500 years ago with some severe trauma. She, too, responded well to the silver plate and expects soon to be returned to full strength. Her problems were exacerbated by a heart weakness. In the course of my dowsing I found that her heart was within the aura of someone who would die in about fifty years, aged forty-two. That it was badly deficient in chromium contributed to her other symptoms. I treated this, too, with other tablets on the silver plate and there was a perceptible improvement in her heart strength and energy levels by the time she came for her second consultation.

Another forty-one-year-old, DS, had a horrible itchy discharge from her ears and none of the specialists she had seen had been able to arrest it. Not life-threatening, it was none the less unpleasant. I found that she, also, had been affected by someone who lived over 95,000 years ago on another planet and who had died at the age of twenty-one from the ear infection which duly left my patient unable to absorb boron and calcium phosphate. The

discharge and irritation in her ears stopped immediately
after I applied the plate with the correct extracting tablets.

Nearly 1,000 years ago someone died at the age of thirty-
two after both their legs were severed in an accident. My
patient, RC, was thirty-two and had endured pains in her
legs for years. They felt as heavy as lead, walking was
painful and running was out of the question. I found that
she was deficient in lithium and vitamins B6 and K. The
lack of this last could have contributed to difficulties in
her reproductive system, the B6 deficiency affected her
nerves, whilst the need for lithium made her energy levels
incredibly unstable. After two hours of treatment with
extracting tablets and the silver plate RC felt very much
better and her legs were longing to be taken for a walk.

At forty-nine SJ didn't know it, but she had a skin
magnetic aura blockage from her throat to her bust. One
hour after her birth she had been 'cleaned up' when her
chest was smeared with zinc and castor oil. The simple,
almost tragic, result was that she was never able to absorb
vitamin C or iodine in that area. It had also rendered her
thyroid gland dysfunctional and she had thus been lacking
in energy all her life. None of the many doctors she had
seen, conventional and alternative, could help and
remained baffled.

   Having realized the problem resided in her
dermatome aura I applied a pad of tablets to her skin
and asked her to sit in my stone circle, holding the
everlasting energy bottles in each hand while the zinc,

iodine and castor oil did their work. Two hours later the entire troubled area of her throat and chest was cleared and restored.

Another patient, BJ, was sixty-eight and I had seen her several times without making much headway in mending her weak heart. Then I discovered that the magnetic field aura of her skin was polluted, again by zinc and castor oil applied when she was a baby. She, too, sat within my stone circle and held the energy bottles. After only an hour her treatment was completed and the heart energy which had only registered at 70 per cent was up to an optimum of 100 per cent.

The dangers of cleansing and 'disinfecting' new babies was brought home to me yet again by the case of HC, who was fifty when I saw her. She had suffered from acidity all her life up till then. After dowsing I found that the solution used to clean her thigh immediately after birth had caused an inability to absorb cadmium which is so important in retaining the body's balance of acidity. After one application of pad and tablets her skin's magnetic field was restored and her system achieved normal alkalinity for, perhaps, the first time in her life.

One patient, WM, had been seeing me for seven years but I had never been able to completely resolve the skin problems which distressed her so. The rashes and eruptions on her body had more or less cleared but I'd been unable to deal with the spots on her face. But once I came to understand the power and influence of the aura, I was able to find, after dowsing, that she was suffering from a pro-incarnation problem of someone due to die at the age of forty-one in about thirty years' time. This defect was cutting off the absorption of sulphur and sodium phosphate to her face now. After application of tablets and the silver plate her skin condition improved quickly and we're confident that the angry redness may yet vanish completely.

In about thirty years' time a twenty-nine-year-old person is going to die. Someone, in other words, who is not yet born. Nevertheless, that person's aura was affecting my patient, NP, who came to me suffering from foot problems: he was losing bone density there as his feet were being drained of carbon and magnesium phosphate. This seepage was also affecting energy leads along the meridian to his brain. I corrected things for him, as I had for many of the others, with the silver plate treatment. His feet are now stronger and his brain energies restored.

I call this sort of work Quantum Leap treatment – and do sometimes wonder and worry about the fate of that person in the future who has yet to learn of their faulty aura. I can only hope that by then there will be many other healers working in this field and that they, too, can cheat 'destiny'. But the effects on a living body can be exactly the same whether they are caused by quantum leaps, reincarnations or influences from other planets.

CHAPTER FIVE

The Power of the Stones

Let me take you into my garden . . .

Only a few years ago I abandoned some holiday plans because a friend insisted I *must* see a stone circle now visible at Gors Fawr in the Prescelly hills in Pembrokeshire, South Wales. Thinking about it now my change of plan seems impulsive, to say the least. Those stones, after all, had stood for thousands of years and would have waited a short while for me to visit at a more convenient time. But such is the power of certain stones that I was impelled, almost commanded, to view them at that precise moment. I was, almost literally, drawn to them and I have never regretted my journey.

I already had an interest in the powers of stones, knowing them to be the ultimate survivors, impacted with ancient experiences and still *alive* with them. A healer friend, GK, a follower of Sathya Sai Baba, had introduced me to the idea that their magnetic and vibrational fields could be harnessed and channelled into our work, so I was already receptive. By then I realized that I must search for and find a wide range of stones and crystals. Each one had to be searched for and dowsed, for not all stones and crystals hold the force I need for my work. I always dowse and select my stones on the basis of their healing force rather than their beauty or perfection. They are then pulverized and added in tablet or tincture form to my armoury of healing treatments. Their extraordinary energies and life forces can make a patient's body more receptive to other remedies that I may well have dowsed for and refined.

But it was that circle in Wales that showed me that the life force in the earth was even more powerful than I had believed before. Already certain of the powers of plants and crystals, I began to learn that a very different, stronger and older healing force was contained in certain stones that contained sun rays and moon rays, concentrated over thousands of years. They release their own vibrational rays and also send that energy into the earth around them. Today I rely on a distillation made from grass clippings taken from the area around my own neolithic circle for many of my most important and effective treatments.

Anyone who has a mindset about the mystic and majestic enormousness of Stonehenge in Wiltshire might be disappointed by the neolithic circle I visited in Wales. The stones there are relatively small, arranged in their circle around a central rock, and display none of the miraculous balancing acts of horizontally placed long stones which characterize Stonehenge. And yet I was immediately struck by the power they generated and began to study that power.

So certain was I of their healing wisdom that soon afterwards I collected similar, smaller stones of the same age and from the same region and arranged them in the ground outside my clinic. Each weighs about five hundredweight but size does not matter: with the right stones you could arrange a circle in your garden or even lay a smaller circle inside your home.

Our forebears' methods were so precise and sophisticated that I am astonished whenever I hear them described as 'primitive'. I can only conclude that they knew and understood many things

Neolithic Healing Circle

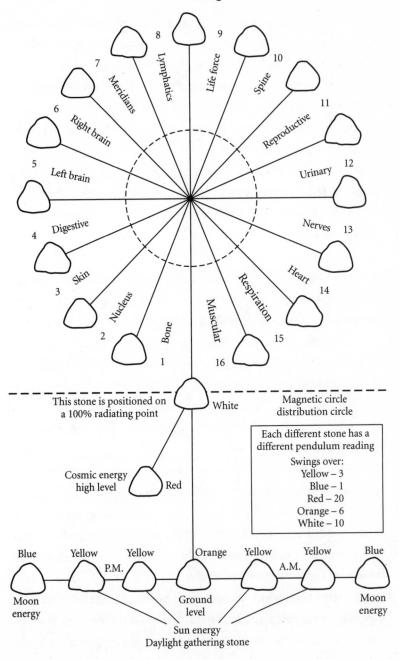

which we today are barely beginning to rediscover. Even with today's wisdom we can only just contemplate how our ancestors found particular rocks and arranged them in a special place.

Stones were used by our neolithic forebears for a variety of purposes. A circle contained the particular energy needed to treat and mend every part of the body system (see Neolithic Healing Circle on page 83). Someone with a broken arm, for instance, would be seated within the circle segment radiating bone energy, with the appropriate herb, plant, flower or leaf wrapped around the injury. A severe head injury was seen to in the corresponding right or left hemisphere of the circle.

At the Prescelly site I counted at least ten circles, each set out with stones weighing upwards of 100 tons apiece, and the energy generated was palpable 1,000 yards away.

It became clear, after intensive dowsing, that our neolithic forebears utilized the different energies of the stones to capture four sources of external energy. One source of energy came from the sun, one from the moon, one from the outer cosmic space, and one from the soil itself. We discovered, by examining the original stones at Gors Fawr, that each stone had a specific form of energy and the simplest form of measuring this is to count the number of swings of the pendulum when held over it.

We also gave each stone a colour for ease of identification. So, when one held the pendulum over the stone, positioned over the 100 per cent radiating point (white), it caused the pendulum to swing ten times. It made ten circles and then stopped. The cosmic high-energy level which we identified as red caused the pendulum to swing twenty times. This energy is picked up from the cosmos and radiated to the 100 per cent radiating point. It is always of a high level, at least four feet off the ground. Therefore, if one holds a pendulum at ground level and gradually raises it vertically, the pendulum does not start swinging until it has reached a height of four feet. One can follow this line of energy like a beam of light. The ground level stone (orange) which has six swings of the pendulum has the ability to gather energy from the sun and moon and convey this energy to the 100 per cent radiating point (white). Holding a pendulum along this line will allow it to swing no higher than ground level, which indicates that the gathering of the energy from the sun and the moon to the ground stone will only convey a low-energy beam to the 100 per cent radiating point. The yellow coloured stones gathering the energy from the sun are specific, and the pendulum will swing over them three times. The yellow stones either side of A.M. on the diagram (see page 83) will pick up the energy of the sun in the morning, and the two P.M. stones will pick it up in the afternoon. When the moon rises in the east there is no transmission from the blue stone at the opposite end until the moon goes round and switches the energy from one to the other. All these stones in turn will transmit energy to the orange and white stones throughout a twenty-four hour clock. The cosmic stone will always radiate energy twenty-four hours a day. Because the sun rises in the east and sets in the west, the beam of light comes from the south and therefore the circle is automatically formed to the north, and the gathering stones are always to the south side of the circle. Immediately the gathering stones are in place, a magnetic circle is formed consisting of fifteen junctions, plus the sixteenth which is the 100 per cent radiating point. The boundary between each junction is marked by a stone, and any stone will do to mark the boundary as no radiating power is required.

Although we have marked out each section equally in our illustration, this is not true in nature. We have already reconstructed three of these circles, each fifty-two feet wide, and each division varies in exactly the same way, with some sections narrow and some much wider. I have no idea of the reason for this.

The phenomenon of this circle is that the larger the stones the larger the circle, and the smaller the stones the smaller the circle. So we have circles formed with a four foot radius which are just as effective as a circle with a fifty-two foot radius – each section has the same specific healing energy. A large circle can transmit its energy over a distance of six miles so that smaller circles can beam in on it and increase their energy without having to have a 100 per cent radiating point.

With a knowledge of anatomy and physiology I went round each section at Gors Fawr and allocated to it a particular part of the body that the energy appears to benefit. This circle has been in use for over three years and I have had no reason to alter this attribution. Arranged around a central stone which draws healing rays from the sun and moon are the sixteen other stones, each one exactly attuned to a vital part of the body – each essential muscle, system, organ or nerve. Their powers are triggered by the central stone and they, in turn, feed the earth around them. I can now dowse to see if that circle segment or anything growing around it can be turned into remedies in my clinic. So dynamic is the force of the stones, so powerful are the healing rays they project, that whatever I plant or grow along those ray paths is extraordinarily potent and effective.

Deep in the soil beneath the stones might lie especially healing fields and elements – the stones send their power downwards as well as outwards, so I dig as well as harvest. And because there is a significant difference between the healing stones and those which generate a different, dynamic life force, I need my pendulum to advise me about which segment to work with for any specific patient. New patients sometimes experience difficulty understanding that every time I apply a healing pad of tablets to their energy system the body has to play its part by supplying its own healing energy to utilize the power in the tablets, and this is where the circle energy becomes vital in my work. Once the circle energy is drawn into the system it fortifies or activates the body's own healing power so that the healing within the tablets can start to work.

Muscle testing is one of the surest ways of demonstrating to sceptics that the sixteen segments of the stone circle radiate energy specifically directed at separate parts of the human body. A sceptic standing in the section of the circle connected to heart strength will find that his or her hand will feel immensely strong when the heart is touched by a tester but that strength will diminish if the tester then touches an unrelated bone. This proves to me the precision in the energy of the segments of the circle. If the 'wrong' part of the body is touched or tested in an inappropriate segment, strength that has been gained is lost.

To express this in a simple and practical way and to demonstrate the inner electricity which we can all harness, I would ask you to imagine one of those gadgets that people use to open their car doors without a key. If the battery of the device is running low the owner simply has to hold it on their chin. A human electric charge will transfer to the gadget and the car doors will open obediently. The same phenomenon occurs in the stone circle: someone with a heart short of energy, like the car door gadget, could stand in the appropriate segment of the circle and be immediately recharged by the power there.

It has taken me some years to come to this understanding but I now have confidence that the stones' energy lines are amazingly powerful and effective. Recently I was enabled to help a child suffering from leukaemia and adjust the imbalance between white cells and red ones by using the stones and their areas of influence correctly.

Even sitting within the circle can be healing. One patient, severely mentally and emotionally disturbed and quite unable to deal with her responsibilities as a wife and mother, was referred to me. After dowsing for the root of her disability I told her she was welcome to sit between two specific stones whenever she liked. Placed there, and absorbing vibrations from two precise fields from time to time over only nine months, she recovered so dramatically that I was able to identify the reasons for her exhaustion, by dowsing, and treat her accordingly. She is now leading a happy and normal life again.

Another patient, an epileptic, had been constrained to control her illness since childhood with drugs which gave her minor but nonetheless distressing side-effects. After spending time seated between the two appropriate stones she was able to reduce her drug intake to the barest minimum and now leads a much fuller and less debilitated life.

I believe that all life on earth could have started with a single cell lodged in the centre of a configuration of rocks, all generating the same cosmic energy that has made us.

If you are contemplating the construction of a circle of your own, at home or in your garden, you must dowse to ascertain the correct order and alignment of your stones – it's a question, yet again, of the 'yes' and 'no' technique as every stone has a different vibrational frequency. Study the diagram on page 83 and remember that the circle should be formed north of the sun, moon, earth and cosmic stones. It will have greater power if the first stone on the circle is sited on an earth point radiating 100 per cent energy – your dowser will guide you. The table in the illustration shows the number of pendulum swings needed to identify each stone needed to form a healing circle.

Anyone can build their own circle once the pendulum is mastered. You don't have to search for rocks or stones in difficult places, or for those with pleasing shapes. All stones are very ancient, and if you can identify their power and arrange them properly your own stone circle will be as effective as mine. Your stones could come from a beach, your garden, a walk on the downs . . . just keep dowsing them until all of the sixteen you need give their answers and form your circle. Many stones will not respond at all because they don't contain the correct magnetic energy or vibrational frequency and these you should discard, with respect. You must be prepared to hunt for and dowse many stones before you find your crucial sixteen and the all-important central one, the 'healing spout'. This will cause the pendulum to swing exactly ten times before abruptly stopping.

The power of stones can be used to form beneficial grids of energy even if you cannot construct a full circle of them. Based on stones erected on Colonsay Island in the Outer Hebrides I have found that six specially dowsed-for stones are adequate. Four of the stones should all have the same power and a pendulum held over each should move in four complete circles and then emphatically stop. The other two stones should cause the pendulum to complete twelve circles before stopping. The first four can now be placed at each corner of a conveniently sized square and the other two sited opposite each other, slightly inwards towards the centre.

And now a steady field of healing energy will be generated. To sit in this small place of peace, wisdom and healing can be a wonderful tonic after a stressful day.

I can't overestimate the benefits of having your own healing circle somewhere at home, for deep relaxation if nothing else. When you have this peaceful, healing source at your disposal you may well find that you can gradually lose and even eventually abandon recourse to chemicals and drugs. Remember that your body belongs to you and need not be handed over to anyone offering artificial 'cures'. A day in bed, plenty of clean, pure water to drink and a peaceful rest amongst or near your stones will help the body to mend itself more often than not.

A garden may be a riot of colour or a place of bosky, mossy greenery. It may be constructed around trees or stones. All have distinct uses and powers far beyond the merely decorative. But above all, perhaps, your garden – however small – can be made into a place of peace.

CHAPTER SIX

Stones, Fossils and Crystals

I have a range of crystals, fossils and stones gathered from all over the world, and each one has a specific use in my healing practice. The very oldest crystals contain many different elements and all can work hard with the body to fight against physical and mental stress. I use crystals to strengthen a patient's aura if it is thin and not protective enough. With a stiffened, mended aura the patient can better resist all kinds of attack.

Crystals can range in shade from purest white to deepest indigo and can be worn decoratively or simply carried and it is important to choose, or be directed, wisely. I know that the wrong crystal can have a weakening effect on the system just as surely as I know what strengths the right one can bestow.

In the spring of 1996 HRH Diana, Princess of Wales wrote to me in thanks for my advice and for the amethyst I had given her. *I will always treasure it and keep it close to my being at all times*, she wrote.

I had found that amethyst was the right crystal for the late Princess of Wales and I know she placed it in a silver container and wore it round her neck. She had come to me troubled by the pressures and demands of her life, fearful and tearful. Afterwards, with the amethyst close to her skin, she gained in strength and confidence and I shall always hope the two are connected. I'd found Diana's crystal in Kathmandu, having gone from place to place before finding a crystal with the healing value I sought. There was a magical property about it but it must have been meant for Diana because I kept it at the clinic for a long time, never tempted to give it away, until the need arose.

I mention this not to be boastful but to emphasize how much suffering can be avoided simply by wearing a crystal. Diana wasn't the only high-profile patient of mine who has found strength this way.

Fossils play another important part in natural healing. If all the original creatures – slugs, fishes and other marine life – survived in the conditions that prevailed on earth so many thousands of years ago, they must have had great protective resistance – traces which I felt could be very useful in dealing with bacteria and viruses today. A knowledge of survival must have been built into the genes of those species and, I reasoned, a memory of their immunity would be contained within their fossils. Homeopathy is the ideal vehicle to transmit that memory.

The fossils, stones and crystals I dowse tell me so much, contain such depths of ancient knowledge. For all were formed from the remains of *survivors*. Whether those remains derive from plant, animal or human life the strain or species which thousands of years later impacted into a hard stone or gleaming crystal constellation represents life that encountered and adapted to illnesses which plague us all to this day.

The trees and plants which grow within the soil where they are buried have been nourished by the strong DNA of those old survivors. Illnesses like leprosy, dysentery, tuberculosis, malaria and leukaemia existed long before we gave them names. And they killed. When I dowse, my pendulum invariably rejects the leaf, bark or flower growing from earth imbued with weak plant or human specimens. It will, however, whirl with wild excitement if it identifies the ancient DNA sent up into a growing thing today from something or someone which had the strength to conquer and survive hundreds or thousands of years ago. Now that strength will nourish any soil and the smallest, slightest plant that blooms and flourishes in it.

Fossils and crystals hold such important keys and messages for our survival today. It's part of my work to unlock and release this old, wise knowledge in an attempt to rekindle and reactivate this knowledge stored in usable form – I never forget that we humans developed from sea creatures or that sea water and sea-cultures like seaweed and algae can be enormously healing. Thus areas like the polders of Holland – long under the North Sea until dam engineering allowed them to be drained and cultivated – are extraordinarily rich. Thousands of Dutch farmers whose fortunes have been made by wonderfully consistent dairy and horticultural crops would probably agree. But, realistically, it is not always convenient for me to examine a seabed and I often find a fruitful place for research is a cemetery or graveyard. This could be a yew-tree shaded quiet English village resting place (where, perhaps, scores of the populace either succumbed to a plague or survived it and died much later), or a graveyard in Egypt where the pines and cedars tell their own stories about the human remains in which they have grown. A memory of health and strength, as well as one of illness and disease, can be recaptured in study of plants and trees growing near to ancient groves and graves.

This conviction that ancient memories of illness and disease can be captured in leaves led me to Cairo. My pendulum knew that in certain graveyards I would find a 'disease memory' to be tapped and the result was a tincture which prolonged a life. I just supplied the patient's system with the DNA message that enabled them to fight the invader. Bugs that had roamed a system for many months and caused conventional doctors to despair responded to fossil memory.

When one considers that one in ten already sick patients picks up some kind of new infection whilst in a British hospital, my approach may come to be regarded with more respect than it sometimes is today. The element palladium plays a large part in the body's system of coping with many bugs, but where in our modern devitalized food is palladium, selenium or chromium, amongst others, to be found?

Aids is a tragedy I am often asked about. Like others, I can give no quick or easy answer. I am however troubled by the fact that Aids sufferers who have come to me seem unwilling to let go of the drugs that earlier doctors have prescribed. One can understand this clinging to a lifeline, any hope of a lifeline. One Aids sufferer who came to me was able to take the leap of faith, discard his drugs and follow my remedies. They didn't save his life, but he lived for some years with lessened pain and debilitation. It's the best I can claim or hope for and the same applies to cancer patients who come to me. I make no promises but can sometimes encourage and facilitate a longer remission than earlier doctors had predicted.

It's often a question of faith and confidence on the part of the patient and their will to live a little longer. One patient who had terrible respiratory problems had to be cleansed of the chemotherapy she had endured before I could help her. We managed, but this situation occurs all too often – the need to banish the stains of drug-related 'cures' before my stone-, fossil- or plant-based healing can play a part in recovery or remission.

A patient with a large tumour on her left brain was sent home from hospital to die but she came to visit me as well. It took months for me to remove residual traces of chemotherapy and other drugs, but eventually the way was clear enough for me to see the cause of the tumour: a pesticide she had used in a holiday bungalow to deal with an earwig infestation. With the aid of my fossil-based tablets the tumour did recede dramatically, but by then my patient had run out of her own healing energy and she died. If I was saddened her family was devastated by her loss but many family members thanked me for my efforts and said how much worse things might have been if they had not all become united in their involvement in her treatments here at the clinic. The patient had been enabled to stay with her family, full of optimism until the last. It struck me how soulless the way that we depart this earth so often is. My patient was too weak to survive but I was assured that her last months were much more comfortable that her hospital might have predicted.

I trust my instincts about particular help for specific patients but cannot claim to understand them beyond accepting that there is a fifth or even sixth dimension that baffles and challenges conventional wisdom and science. I have observed it at work too often to be dismissive. Why on earth should industrially researched and funded, packaged and advertised drugs, sold with incentives to hospitals and GPs, be more effective than the natural remedies I seek? One of the ironies, of course, is the fact that many a potent plant or mineral-based formula is tampered with and tempered by these international drug giants and, under a fancy scientific name, sold as a miracle cure to practitioners all over the world. The basics in the medicine work hard to do their best, and often succeed, but they have really been garnered in the name of profit, not well-being.

Crystals are lovely things and can light up a neck or face with their sparkle: I have no problem with their use in jewellery and the cheer that they can endow that way. I'm not a miner and I'm pleased to find my crystals in Hatton Garden, shops in Paris, Scotland or the East. Often the cheapest crystals found in markets or bazaars have the strongest healing power and in their very 'imperfection' resides some special strength. Here it is not a matter of price, but of value. It takes some skill to recognize this. Folklore often speaks to us of the vision of the crystal ball and whilst not subscribing to that kind of fairground blarney I do believe that crystals have incredible powers and knowledge. In Tel Aviv once I was searching and dowsing for five special crystals to help patients with traumas. I found a shop and spoke to the owner, whom I had not dealt with or seen before. He told me that he had not been planning to be there that day and said that when he had been in Russia he had been offered small pieces of meteorite and bought them with a sense that someone might be interested one day. I then produced a fragment of meteorite of my own, deficient in energy, and found that my new friend's meteorite matched my own exactly, except that its energies were stronger and thus better for patients' needs. My shopkeeper friend also showed me a crystal he had bought with me in mind in Romania. I guess this says a little about human thought and kindness, as well as coincidence. Merely by touching that particular stone, indeed a precious one, I can see if a patient has a tendency towards leukaemia.

Again by coincidence – or perhaps by some strange design – another healer visited that shop on the same day, seeking a remedy for his painful back. Empowered as I was just then I was able to help this fellow-healer on the spot. The aura of all the many crystals in the shop was powerful and ready to be tapped.

Something similar took place in Kuala Lumpur when I visited

a crystal shop. The owner was there: something had impelled him to postpone his flight to Java and go, instead, to work that day when I stopped by and began to dowse for what I needed. He was able to show me that my pendulum would have trouble searching through the heavy plate glass behind which many of his stones were stored and with his unexpected help I was able to find the very one I needed.

The owner was a very heavy smoker and had asked me why he was so dependent on the weed. I told him that he had received a severe shock about eight years before. He then pulled up his shirt and displayed a large hole in the middle of his back, explaining that he had been shot eight years earlier, during a robbery. We became great friends after that and he has offered me the chance of opening clinics in the Far East, in association with a doctor friend of his. One of these days, perhaps . . .

Another time, in Morocco, I'd planned to hire a driver and a jeep to take me into the desert to find a special fossil which would complete the formula of five items which I had travelled to North Africa to assemble. Fully prepared for a four-hour drive into the interior and having told my driver, broadly, what I was looking for, I was surprised when he quickly pulled up at a scrappy market and directed me to a small shop. There I dowsed and found exactly the fossils I needed.

I have found that such generous, if subconscious, impulses are very powerful indeed and it is these which confirm, over and over again, my belief and faith in that sixth sense. It only seems to hold if an individual's motives are true, strong and guided by some greater good. The frequency with which I find that some stranger's accidental impulse can lead to the healing of some far away and unknown patient of mine is quite extraordinary. It is worth remembering that crystals were formed within stones during some crucial moment when the Earth's character was shifting, molten perhaps, or fashioned by some dramatic, magnetic lightening strike. Thus those fossils and crystals contain the positive energy of a renewed and regenerated planet and the power trapped within that molten transformation remains in place for us to tap now.

In Malta I was able to identify five stones and leaves which, once pulverized and made into tablets to be strapped across the skin near the heart, helped a patient with a heart valve problem. As always when travelling I had taken hair and nail clippings of patients whom I hoped to help. This means I can identify the exact remedies needed by each patient. One particular patient's hospital doctors, monitoring his 'progress' as he cycled on a machine after my trip, were astonished by the improvement in his strength and heart-rate. I have to report – without pleasure or particular pride – that his doctors were reluctant to accept that my alternative therapy had contributed to his recovery. They were, I understood, positively unwilling to accept that my Maltese-formula tablets had helped more than their chemical ones. This is something that I have learned to expect. Fortunately I have an unusually enlightened and expert chemist in London who has for years now dealt with my stones, barks and plant clippings and makes the tablets that have proved to be so helpful to so many. Thus I don't have to wait long for the remedy to be available. And nor do my patients.

Not long afterwards a patient came to me complaining about a leaky bladder sphincter muscle, causing her water to dribble out. Incontinence is not exactly life-threatening, but it's very distressing all the same. My honeysuckle flower remedy did the trick: the sphincter muscle regained strength and she has regained control not only of her bladder but of her life. I had sat in a friend's garden not long before, with this patient's problem at the back of my mind. My friend waved at her tumbling trellis of honeysuckle and had no idea that three or four particular blooms could help my patient. But the pendulum knew and by the coincidence of that meeting I was able to gather flowers specifically containing the ingredients that the bladder problems required. And the resultant tincture may well go on to help others with similar problems. I had just happened to be in the right garden at the precise moment those particular flowers bloomed, nourished by some unique combination of elements deep in the soil. Since such incidents are by no means uncommon my belief in the benign power of coincidence is ever strengthened.

Not long ago a young father from Finland, hearing about my work on that strange grapevine that creates all manner of links, brought his daughter to me. The child was crippled by infantile paralysis (polio) – a condition seldom seen these days, thank goodness. I quickly saw that the little girl's paralysis was rooted in a spot behind her left eye but also knew that this area would be tricky to reach. My pendulum eventually instructed me to find help in Guernsey and was quite specific about the day I should go there. And speaking of specifics – think twice about any commercial blarney you might read: each individual needs a different crystal to identify their problems and no one stone can help in a general way. By no means dismiss the power of faith but place your faith as carefully as you can.

The father of my Finnish patient had faith, was prepared to wait and agreed that I should fly to Guernsey exactly twenty-five days later. On that day, having dowsed the island, I found that an extraordinary and rare low tide took place in a certain bay. Striding across the sand, for miles it seemed, the pendulum suddenly quickened and at a particular spot it located a small, seldom exposed area of sand which contained the very elements and minerals which were required. I collected it, called Finland and made up the tablets. These were applied to the child's face, near the eye area where I believed the problem originated. Her blockage was cleared and within weeks her legs started to move. This is yet another example of the healing powers contained within the sea. We underestimate them at our peril.

Stones and bones, then, hold the keys and answers to questions of survival. Remains of creatures and living elements that survived against all the old ancient odds hold essential signals that we need today. We just have time to renew our inherited powers of survival and to renew that great load of expert fossil knowledge. Even 'modern' illnesses such as asthma can be handled and controlled by the old wisdom of the stones and plants if only we ask them to release it. The trees, the stones and, perhaps above all, the sea and its spiny creatures can teach us how to overcome the ailments that the modern world has imposed. Never forget that *your* DNA is that of generations of strong survivors and that you have inherited the strength to beat virtually anything that the natural or industrial world can throw at you. The human blueprint hasn't altered much over all these years: we just need to recognize its shapes and colours again and get our stony, fossilized forebears to help us if need be. Even an illness like tuberculosis can be stanched with wisdom and the patient's will to survive. I have seen too much evidence and proof of this power to even think of apologizing for these remarks now.

Sometimes I'm asked if sunlight helps and heals us. I know and believe that the force of sunshine entering a stone or plant is vital, but I don't think much of its effects on the human skin. Thus I take little notice of the modern preoccupation with SAD (seasonal affective disorder). There are now 4,000 recorded cases of malignant melanoma in the UK each year. If you decide not to stay out of the sun, try to fortify your system with an equal mix of homeopathic vitamin A and safflower oil. My holiday kit always includes these and I suck a tablet every thirty minutes or so when I'm in the sun. The sun's rays form potentially harmful vitamin D in the skin and the vitamin A and safflower oil can soak up and balance the effects. I also apply watermelon suntan lotion to all exposed areas for the first few days of a hot holiday and my skin is never blemished or burned.

I have far more trust and faith in the constants of old stones and their abilities to gather and store such benevolent forces as sunlight. The Prescelly stones from Wales which stand in a circle outside my clinic and which have lent their absorbed forces to many of my patients give proof of this.

Nature is unpredictable and paradoxical, like human beings. Some lead is poisonous, badly affecting brain and memory, but lead plumbum is life-saving. The same applies to pure mercury, which can benignly influence our long – medium – and short-term memory but when used by dentists in the form of Mercoam to fill teeth has a tendency to leak into the system and cause distortion inside the cells and the blood. We must always be careful about the use of such elements and respects all their powers – both good and harmful.

But this I know: within the magnetic aura of our stones, stored and blessed with the sun's energy over many centuries, planted seeds will grow more quickly and flourish as if they had been nurtured in a greenhouse. Within the neolithic grid of the stones an earlier, longer, warmer and more magnetic fertile field will be spread.

On this I can say little more here. The memories of the stones remain marvellously mysterious to me. The leaves of one tree, the *Gingko biloba*, strangely resemble the shape of the human brain. Combined with certain other leaves and cactus extracts, they are one of the most effective healing things on earth I know.

CHAPTER SEVEN

We Are What We Eat

It's blindingly obvious and, by now, accepted by almost everyone that what we eat and drink affects not only our appearance but our health, strength and general sense of well-being, physical and psychological. My attitude to diet, however, differs crucially from many routines and regimes advanced by others.

Firstly, I do not promise or even invariably recommend weight loss. That the course I advise often results in weight reduction may please some of my patients but is something of a bonus or side issue: I am much more interested in striving towards the holistic restoration of total health. When a system is re-educated by correct nutrition the likely result is a more toned as well as a stronger body. I have had patients whose total food intake wouldn't nourish a sparrow, yet their weight was enormous: non-absorption of the B vitamin inositol, fat and salt as well as poisons held in suspension by body fat can cause excess weight. But not everyone was born to be svelte and sinewy. Indeed, I have seen many patients whose overall health has been damaged in the quest for a body-shape which is, for them, quite unnatural.

Secondly, few dieticians believe, as I do so strongly, that what we put into our mouths, and which is then processed slowly round the internal – and miraculously designed – system, will respond to our body's ancient and unique DNA. Each food we take in should be as pure as possible and compatible with whatever already exists in our blood, bones, tissue and ancestral programming. I prescribe diet after I have identified a physical dysfunction. I dowse to return any patient, literally, to their fundamental DNA and any remedial nutrition I advocate is part of a broader treatment for illness, disability or stress.

A word here about antibiotics, those sacred saviours upon which much conventional modern medicine depends. Antibiotics are known to zap certain bacteria but most of us today know that they can develop spirited resistance and continue to flourish, thus creating a need for a stronger drug to quash them. This, in turn, will be overcome by bacteria and yet another antibiotic will be required . . . As antibiotics are basically fungi, a body persistently treated with them will soon become the host to cultures which, in my view, actively breed new strains of bacteria which the immune system cannot recognize. This will result in clusters of simmering bacteria invading the body and continuously draining the patient of energy.

All this is a little ironic as most of us were brought up to have faith in Alexander Fleming's breakthrough in the 1920s when he identified a mould culture which became known as penicillin and undoubtedly saved thousands of lives. We were all thus programmed to regard subsequently developed antibiotics as tremendously beneficial. But we didn't realize then that the body's systems, particularly the lymph system, are choked by such drugs and rendered unable to cleanse and heal themselves. And thus challenged, our immune systems need stronger drugs to fight the bacteria which can attack at any time.

There is *always* some bug or other going around. Your friends may be laid low, feel seedy, be off work or out of commission socially. But you have been spared and can function normally. This is because, at that time, your body was strong enough to resist this week's or this month's debilitating strain. We are all likely to succumb to a bug when we are weakened or exhausted. It is my belief that a cleansed and strong body will continue to resist and that resorting to possibly damaging antibiotics can thus be avoided.

In Fleming's day it was, correctly in my view, regarded as important to keep a patient cool – and particularly their head. Mothers then would sit by their children and wipe their brows with a cool damp flannel. A strict diet containing no carbohydrates or proteins would be offered, and water and fruit juices would help to cleanse the system. In this way, in what used to be called a 'nature cure', the body fought back and cleansed itself. It was against, or rather within, this knowledge that Fleming worked. The two essentials addressed were purification and corrected digestion. This could take time.

But much of Alexander Fleming's wisdom has been lost or set aside in the international drug giants' searches for a quick fix and instant cure. The big companies may well help to keep alive those who have seriously and serially abused their bodies, but are not really the friends of those who are basically healthy and simply need a more natural remedy to restore them to the health that their body can achieve. We don't need to buy (on prescription or over the counter) expensive but valueless medicines when a decent diet will protect us from most ailments. It's all too easy to digest the 'we know best' views of the medical profession. *It is time for the individual to take more responsibility for their health and body.*

The Soil Association was founded over fifty years ago, in Suffolk, England, to promote organic farming. But as farmers and growers must allow land to lie fallow in grass for three years in order to become organic it is perhaps unsurprising that many are slow to take up that challenge, even if their fields can be sown with not-very-profitable crops for cattle feed. Grants are now being offered by the British Government to encourage organic growing. Even the water companies are looking at the practices of farmers and growers over the large catchment areas that feed into their underground reservoirs.   There is now talk of the water companies encouraging these farmers to eliminate the use of pesticides and chemical sprays and go over to organic farming. With the aid of this umberella support large areas of land can be reclaimed and, in due course, will be fit for cultivating nutritious crops and raising happier and healthier cattle.   However, the nutritional value of all crops grown must rely on the DNA of the seeds sown to produce the crops.

Organic farmers and growers need to have yields equal to chemically grown produce to remain in business. These yields can only be derived from seeds that have been genetically engineered. In the last generation or two our plant breeders have concentrated on hybridizing, which is slightly different from genetic engineering – they were able to clone the seed to reproduce vegetables exactly the same size to mature at exactly the same time. This development has meant, in my experience, that the ability of the vegetable to pick up its nutrients from the soil has been altered, and quite often the nutrient level of vegetables without the gene instruction inside is almost negligible. The EU is now trying to standardize vegetables throughout the EC by regulation. I spoke to one of our leading plant breeders over thirty years ago and asked why he couldn't breed for vitamin and mineral content. 'Jack,' he said, 'we are only asked to breed for shape and colour and crops that can mature and be harvested to a timetable.' Nothing much has changed. The vitamin and mineral content of most crops is still not considered in many of our plant-breeding programmes. I suggest that open pollinated seeds should be used when growing for oneself and the only source of such seed is the Henry Doubleday Seed Bank. Here one can obtain seeds which have been naturally selected and still contain the inbred information on the job of the plant to search for and bring up and put into the leaves of the plant the nutrients that lie in the soil underneath. This is not happening in the hybrid or genetically engineered seeds.

The poorer the soil the worse the crop, however brightly the produce may shine beneath the supermarket cellophane or how creamily delicious the non-organic dairy produce may seem to be. But we *are* getting somewhere. Slowly, perhaps, I think people are realizing that their apples, cabbages and tomatoes need not be of the same size. The notion of the hybrid seed for foodstuffs is less fashionable than it was – just as many people prefer a rambling rose to a stiff flower-show hybrid candidate.

Don't imagine that all vegetables are good for you. Sad to say cauliflower is best avoided, especially the clean white heads sold – often under cellophane, which is itself full of transferable impurities – in supermarkets. Any sign of caterpillar droppings spells doom for a grower supplying cauliflowers to these emporia of cleanliness. Thus growers, for their own protection and livelihood, make sure that each cauli head is clinically clean and the substances they use for this purpose are insecticides.

Public obsession with *apparent* cleanliness and purity is a terrible irony when so many vegetables and fruits thus wrapped are actually poisonous. At the very least it is worth dowsing for yourself along the supermarket shelves. The answer, of course, is that the organic food industry should expand and the more organic food is demanded the quicker we will all be able to benefit from it. It's interesting to note that much of the pathetically low percentage of organically rich soil in Britain, formed originally from the dispersal of the ice age which left vast quantities of very fertile soil, is in Ayrshire, the West Country and Gower and along the East Anglian coast – areas where people do tend to live longer than those elsewhere in the UK. Perhaps it is also significant that in these coastal areas people have better access to fresh fish. And longevity worldwide is frequently marked by a diet rich in iron, selenium, chromium and magnesium – all of whose absences I can dowse for, identify and supply. The importance of olive oil in the diet should not be dismissed. Recent surveys have shown that the Mediterranean diet, rich in olives and olive oil, and the Cretan diet in particular, may be linked to longer than average lifespans in those areas.

Often I see whole families together or parents who are worried about their children's general health and progress. I know it's a struggle for them, but I urge them to try to help their children to resist peer group pressure to eat the wrong things – junk food, usually. The food they put on the family table must be tasty as well as sustaining and meal times thus enjoyable affairs. This may not stop the son or daughter rebelling by spending pocket money on fizzy drinks and synthetic candy bars, but at least it's a step towards damage limitation. I believe parents and children should eat the same foods and that parents should at times exercise their right to lay down the law about eating habits – as I did with my three. I'm quite convinced that some vandalism and antisocial behaviour in young people stems from their poor diet, and unashamedly believe that sometimes it is necessary to be 'cruel to be kind' if the result of the diet is a child both physically and mentally integrated and balanced. Put quite simply, a mother who is strained and worried about her child's constant ill-health or poor performance at school is more likely to generate the family tensions which may lead to antisocial behaviour than one who is calm and confident about her son or daughter's development. I can't adequately stress the importance of diet in this. And, of course, the earlier a young person's body is educated to absorb the right nutrients and reject damaging matter the better.

Buy and choose wisely and carefully, from shops selling organically produced goods if possible. Yes, as I said before, these products might be a little more expensive, but I believe them to be cheap at the price.

I realize that some of the foods and remedies that I recommend are more expensive to buy and more trouble to find than foods that might be in the larder now, but I know that the extra, and relatively small, expense, is worth it. It is never too late to change dietary habits. Recently an eighty-four-year-old woman came to me near to despair about the dismal quality of her existence. One session was sufficient to drain enough poison from her system to give her immediate strength and the optimism to see that following my dietary advice would compound the improvement. If she'd had a microwave oven I would have advised her to throw it away as the rays in these devices do not merely destroy many of the nutrients in the food under preparation but add destructive elements which the body must struggle to cope with. Another patient, aged ninety, suffered from asthma, back pain, walking difficulty, muscle strain, digestive problems and poor hearing. After eight months of treatment and diet adjustment his pains and other afflictions had vanished and now he walks two miles every day.

I believe that the blueprint of our genetic programming for longevity can be altered, partly by diet. But there is no point in enduring a long, debilitated and miserable old age. The more fragile an elderly person is the more likely they are to develop chronic but not necessarily life-threatening illnesses.

It's sometimes a matter of faith. I realize that, with older people in particular, it is difficult to shake off the ideas, beliefs and trust in conventional medicine that they were brought up to respect, if not actually revere. But I believe that the 'miracle' drugs which were supposed to represent such breakthroughs in the treatment of diseases like rickets and tuberculosis sometimes left a sinister legacy of time bomb side-effects which had to be addressed later. And I appreciate that it takes courage – or desperation – to confront this.

The routine that works for me is to have a 'mini-fast' of fifteen hours every day. I don't eat upon rising but I'll have some vegetable juice and a spoonful of either nitrogen-free linseed oil, olive oil or cod-liver oil in three-day rotation. I also take some psyllium husk for roughage and fibre. These help to keep limbs and joints healthy as well as encouraging the bowels. My *break fast* is a light meal at noon. I usually have an organic salad of raw vegetables and some crispbread or brown pitta bread, perhaps with a smear of butter, half a pound of which will last me a fortnight. For a healthy heart I take chromium and selenium tablets too. With the benefit of dowsing I can select red wine, some of which has the ability to strengthen the heart. At the moment I find there is a very nice French wine which suits the purpose, called Cotes du Rousillon.

In the evening I will feast! More organic vegetables – carrots, leeks, potatoes, greens and parsnips, perhaps, with some eggs, liver, fish, organic chicken or lamb or soft goat's cheese. This I will take with more vegetable juice. I sometimes have some pure vanilla ice cream or some honey – it is rare for me to eat sweets or cakes but I do nibble on a lot of nuts, Brazils, cashews and walnuts, so I get plenty of good protein. All my family has thrived on this sort of diet. Even before recent scares I was emphatic that beef and pork raised in confined herds were both off-limits. When I was younger I enjoyed many of the more familiar sweet and energy-producing foods and I even thought that they were doing me good. Now I know that all the energy and sweet treats I require can come from a different kind of diet.

I realize that this diet may seem unappetizing to some but taste buds can be re-educated and the judicious use of herbs and seasonings results in truly tasty food and the feeling of well-being derived surely outweighs the occasional desire for something creamy or a slab of chocolate? And this sort of diet doesn't have to be antisocial, either. In a restaurant I can dowse the menu (I have learned how to do this under the table if I must, undetected by waiters), and choose a dish from the menu which will enhance rather than damage health. Remember that eating out can be at the root of severe food poisoning, so it's always worth passing a finger over the food in question and dowsing simultaneously beneath the table if you have already ordered but are still concerned. To guard against *E. coli* bacteria I always look out for Jerusalem artichokes or take tablets containing them. This vegetable is rich in bifido-bacteria and without these the protective acidophilus – which fights food poisons such as *E. coli* – cannot thrive.

I always take a daily range of supplements. One, called Algivit, is derived from the sea. Another, Spirulina, is used in conjunction with a Nepalese herb, guduchi, and I call this Biolina/Guduchi. These two supplements, along with some others, supply my system with a wide range of absorbable vitamins and elements from natural sources. Dowsing tells me that most people here are walking around with thirty absorbable elements in their systems. And yet the body is capable of utilizing well over a hundred elements. A study of different national diets and health levels offers illumination: the typical Japanese diet provides about sixty and when dowsing in Nepal I found that in eating foods grown at home or from home-grown selected seeds the general population had about ninety absorbable elements.

I seldom, if ever, prepare a diet sheet for a patient, but I *do* offer broad guidelines. Certain preparations like evening primrose oil, taken daily, can never do any harm and will benefit many – not just the menopausal women for which it is so widely recommended. I will advise about vitamin supplements when I have dowsed the individual patient and I always advise specific brands because some products on the market are far less pure and effective than others. The important thing is to enable the body – by the drainage of toxic barriers – to absorb the elements and minerals I advise. Once effectively broken down by these means fat waste is extruded or otherwise released by the re-educated body.

Sometimes it's necessary for me to enable the dermis to release fatty or other toxins because the skin has thickened. This thickening is often the result of having had a general or even local anaesthetic in the past. Now I try to change the mindset – brain waves, if you like – which have caused this and will give and sometimes also prescribe treatments which will break down these skin barriers so that toxins can be released through layers of untoughened skin. Remember that 60 per cent of the body's energy goes straight to the brain and this magnificent organ has control over not merely our thinking and intellectual capacities but over every other function and activity.

Sometimes I meet a patient who has had a cancer diagnosed by some other physician. That patient may have had surgery, or be in remission or worried about a recurrence of the condition. I'm concerned about any 'magic' cancer cure, including the use of drugs like Interferon, because I believe that a chemical solution is rarely a cure: a different way of looking at internal causes and blockages is preferable. This philosophy applies, in the main, to all my treatments. So I don't treat an illness, but a blockage – the blockage that allowed the separate illness to develop. I have had some successes.

Many patients suffer from colon problems but the source of the discomfort can be residual in the bronchials or pleura. Modern paints, asbestos and bottled gas fumes can all settle in the chest and cause colonic problems. Vaccines in the humerus (the upper arm) can also deprive the colon, small intestine and lungs of energy. They can also relay the DNA of the poison to other parts of the system. Thus lung cancer can be caused by residual poison in the humerus. Heavy legs and bulging veins can be caused by the base of the cerebral canal becoming loaded with hair dyes and bleach. Gout in the large toe can be traced back to the liver through the meridian line – the link between a damaged liver and gout has long been established . . .

The list below is merely a sample of the types of poisons I see and deal with every day and, sadly, that list never seems to stop growing.

Poisonous substances taken out of patients

aluminium sulphate (a vaccine carrier)

bleach

black dye (from stockings)

Carbaryl (for hair nits)

cholera vaccine

cleaning fluid

clothing dye

diptheria, tetanus and whooping cough vaccine

formaldehyde (a vaccine carrier)

hair dye

junine poison (from rat droppings)

lacquer (hair spray)

lead (from paint and the water supply)

Mercoam (from tooth fillings)

meningitis vaccine

nitrous oxide (laughing gas)

nicotine (from cigarettes)

nylon (from clothing)

petroleum ointment

polio vaccine

rubber molecules

Septrin (an antibiotic)

slimming drugs

smallpox vaccine

TB vaccine

tulip bulb poison (from eating bulbs)

zinc poison (from buckets)

Over the years I have changed my views about fasting. As a much younger man I would often cleanse my body of toxins by going several days – sometimes as long as two weeks – without food. Water and a little pure fruit or vegetable juice were taken, but nothing else. I still believe that fasting is a marvellous way of flushing poisons out of the body, but it must be very carefully monitored, and I would not recommend anyone going on a fast of more than a day or two to do so without supervision. The furred tongue, nasty breath and possible light-headedness which often result are of less importance than the overall weakness and strains on bodily reserves. By all means reduce and regulate the diet for a short time but don't ignore the system's need for correct nourishment. I seem to do quite well on my fourteen moderate meals a week, supplemented with the husks and seeds which we all need to add the bulk and fibre required to cleanse the system each day.

Nor would I advocate fasting for children, although I believe that a fevered child will respond well to a short period (no more than twenty-four hours) of fluids-only nutrition before they are gently fed some solids. Some texts published in the 1930s and 1940s, and still in print, extol the benefits of fasting for pregnant women and I cannot agree with this, either. For most adults a short period of lighter than usual diet with carefully balanced foods, perhaps with extra nutrients in tablet or powdered form, is generally enough to stimulate the body into cleansing itself. We must remember that the body needs its fuel and energy, so observe its signs and listen to its signals.

The words 'fasting' and 'feasting' are interestingly similar. Both extremes can have adverse affects and now that I know so much more about correct day-to-day nutrition than I did when I was younger I feel less certain that the former should counterbalance the latter.

We all know that the 'breakfast' is the meal which ends the fasting after yesterday's evening meal and the night. Many nutritionists insist that breakfast is the most important meal of the day and should not on any account be missed. I think it rather depends upon whether you are desk bound or involved in physically strenuous work and thus need the early calories. In this, as in every aspect of my book, I would ask you to think about and even challenge conventional wisdoms. Listen to your body. Trust your brain.

CHAPTER EIGHT

Organics

Most of us can picture Jerry Hall, the rangy Texan fashion model who has remained at the top of a notoriously fickle profession for two decades now. The glorious long tawny hair, the endless legs, the warm and confident smile are her hallmarks, so to speak, and perhaps it is the sense of a person behind the pictures and the 'personality' which have helped to keep Jerry on the covers of the glossies so consistently.

Few realize, however, that behind every stride down a catwalk, every pose for a magazine photographer and every immaculately clad and shod society appearance and smile lay excruciating back pain. The births of her children with Mick Jagger did little, of course, to reduce this. Jerry had suffered for twenty years at least. Her mother and sisters too had, unsurprisingly, the identical DNA sections which caused the back pains. Jerry reported that her agony was lifted after one session with me – during which I advised a radical shift towards an organic diet – and has not returned. Interestingly enough, Jerry and Mick proudly announced another pregnancy soon afterwards.

I realized that in her case any dowsing would focus on the tip of the nose or finger – not the back itself as one might suppose. Again my knowledge of the body's meridian lines enabled me to ascertain where the root of a problem was expressed, along with the messages emanating from the hair and fingernail clippings. I saw Jerry shortly before I had come to fully appreciate the importance of analysing a patient's aura, but even so, her progress was swift. My pendulum supplied the answers. I always use the patient's hair and nails to connect with the theta – the part of the brain that holds the memory of the needs and mistakes of generations past and can suggest adjustments and remedies.

None of those patients who were treated by me before I fully understood the importance of auras should fear that they did not receive my best – all forms of medicine evolve over time and I'm pleased to report that my learning curve did not reach a plateau years ago, as happens with some doctors, and that I remain ever open to new ideas and procedures. To worry about that would be as fruitless as worrying about being successfully treated for some dietary problem years ago, before it was realized that organic short cuts were just around the corner. No – my more recent work with auras has simply helped me to analyse and deal with illnesses more quickly: I think I would have arrived at the same conclusions, eventually prescribed much the same for the patient in the past. In fact my understanding of auras has confirmed the worth of much that I have believed for years.

I cannot stress enough the importance of acknowledging the wisdom of our cells' and genes' ancient memories. I was able to dowse for the causes of Jerry's problem, and those of her family, and prescribe organic and homeopathic remedies which seem to have worked. Here, however, I want to attempt a brief explanation of the organic systems which proved to help Jerry Hall and her family, some of whom later consulted me.

Firstly I must dowse to discover whether a problem has arisen during a patient's lifetime or whether it was inherited. Did the problem begin in the womb or was it passed on by generations past? If so, was it on the father's or the mother's side? These questions apply to a person's physical body, but as an earlier chapter relates, we are influenced by another, even more complex, series of forces – those of our auras. All of us are surrounded by these invisible past and future ghosts, some benign and some malign where our health is concerned. Only when I am informed by the pendulum can I hope to prescribe successfully. Each question which I ask of it can lead to a direct answer about why some specific area of the system is failing to function normally.

It generally comes down to what the patient or their forebears have been consuming, and this links directly to the organic growing and farming which I regard as so important today. There is never an escape from the past but inherited malfunctions can be corrected, as I have seen time and time again.

Someone from Norway or Sweden may bear the legacy of the whale blubber that dominated the diet and smoke from tallow candles breathed in there for so long. An Irish patient's problem could relate to potato, bracken or poteen poisoning, again established many generations ago. It is thus important (but not always imperative) for me to learn about national diet and my patient's family background: these, after all, are legitimate short cuts. I can usually dowse successfully for a patient who has been adopted, for instance, even if they don't have accurate information about their biological parents. It makes no difference to me as I can always dowse for the roots of a patient's genetic history.

By now readers will know the emphasis I place on the quality of the soil in which the food we eat is grown and farmed and upon which organically reared cattle and other livestock graze. Even if they can't visit me or another similar healer it *is* within their power to take care and choose organically produced meat, fish and other goods in shops and supermarkets, to decline inferior foods and to grow good fruit and vegetables at home, even if they have only a tiny space or plot. Above all, reject anything which has been fed and 'nourished' with artificial chemicals, for these synthetics destroy the precious organic mulch which is steeped into the soil and is perhaps the most valuable legacy of our forebears.

Decades ago a remote region of Poland was peasant poor but healthy. Cancer was almost unknown in the province. Then after the 1939 invasion and the introduction of 'modern' farming and cropping methods which involved the ploughing into the land of factory-based fertilizers, the soil became contaminated with carcinogenic *Aspergillus flavus* alkaloids and cancers were increasingly identified. This seemed to go hand in hand with the introduction of canned foods to the small local shops and markets.

The fragrant smoke emitted from those logs burning in your grate may well come from a tree that stood for centuries and drew strength from earth enriched by the 'skeletons' of older trees which were, in turn nourished by plant, insect and human remains. Every gardener knows something of the use and value of compost and manure – 'muck-spreading', for want of a less scientific expression. I want to advance the idea that what is considered OK for the garden flowers is also a good idea for humans. It's rather a shame that 'soil' has become synonymous with 'dirty' in our language and culture. Organically rich soil can nourish us all.

I found the case of my patient BM rather ironic in this context.

She was understandably worried about an outbreak of moles beneath her breastbone. They were becoming steadily thicker, irritated and more numerous. I found that this nasty outbreak was not pre-cancerous (as she had feared), but connected to a blockage in the coronal suture of the brain caused by a tetanus injection some years earlier. Aluminium sulphate was the carrier of the vaccine and had caused a deficiency in PABA, known to be a cause of dark moles and speckles. I applied the appropriate tablet pads below her breast and the moles retreated. Before long they should disappear. The irony here is that people often still rush to get a tetanus jab from their GP if they have so much as grazed their skin with a rose thorn (an old rusty nail may be another matter), assuming that soil is dirty and poisonous. The reality is that the vaccine's chemicals are far more likely to do harm.

Of course it is not simply a matter of what we have on our plates and place in our mouths. Organic considerations extend beyond this. The colour, texture and strength of your hair is as much an inheritance as the shape of your nose. Don't damage it with chemical dyes: many problems with my female patients can be dowsed back to their late teens, when they first started to experiment with hair colourants. Others connect back to early teens of both sexes when they had the then obligatory BCG vaccine against tuberculosis. Others I associate with diphtheria jabs given at the age of three months. Often the sixth month of a pregnancy can trigger a dangerous time bomb as this is when many women, tired, fed up, feeling grumpy and lumpy try to cheer themselves up with a visit to a hairdresser, not realizing that the very atmosphere there (all that ammonia . . .), let alone the treatments they pay so handsomely for, is damaging their health and that of their baby.

An organic diet is fantastically helpful in restoring the body's balance but I respect the importance of our skin. This is why so many of my remedies are designed and tailored to extract poisons via the homeopathic tablets strapped to the skin and others taped there for absorption. It's a long time since I used soap in the bath. I enjoy a hot soak as much as anyone, but I know that the essential waterproofing of the outer dermis can be damaged by commercial soaps. Pure soap is a different matter but can still be hard to track down. Much depends, of course, on the quality of your local tap water, but if you find that a soapy lather is hard to rinse away, try putting organic lemon juice and skins in the bathwater, remembering that most commercial soaps – however prettily scented and packaged – are probably made from organically unfriendly products. Another vicious circle may then begin to spin: something in the soap or bath gel seems to have caused itchy or flaking skin, so you go to the chemist for some emollient which contains chemicals which in turn sink into the skin and create problems of their own – although you may not realize this until much later when you have trouble with seemingly unrelated problems, perhaps with your physical balance or blood pressure. Some days I put a few drops of a special oil in the bathwater. Other times I might strew in some calcified seaweed.

I cannot stress strongly enough the benefits of seaweed products. As a market gardener I recognized the value of seaweed as a fertilizer, and now I know that its elements and strengths can enter my pores whilst I bathe, cleansing my body by extracting toxins. Don't, however, imagine that gulping handfuls of kelp tablets will do the same trick: internally taken seaweed needs to be broken down by nitrogen, and such tablets, even from reputable health stores, can rob the body of an essential beneficial source.

There is something in those old stories about the virtues of sea air and a holiday by the coast. It wasn't just the seaweed that the children delighted in, fishing from the rock-pools, or the rest and relaxation of the family break – even now the sea is so rich in protected minerals and elements, evaporated into the beach air by sunshine and warmth, and so dense with relatively pure ions, the seabed relatively undisturbed, that it is no surprise that most people feel rested, even restored after a time near the coast. Seawater, after all, contains every single nutrient known to meet our needs. (Bear in mind, though, that swimming should only take place in unpolluted waters.)

A last word on the subject of seaweed. Fifty years ago the glorious Jersey Royal potatoes were thus fertilized. These days the spuds are chemically grown and harvested and it is a sad comment on the quality and taste – or lack of it – in other British crops – that Jerseys still command a premium price. Our tastebuds' slip is showing . . . Buy Cyprus or Egyptian potatoes instead, so long as they are organic. Half the price, twice the taste and less likely to have been chemically enforced.

If you have a garden, of any size, remember that nothing should be wasted. Buy a shredder if necessary to pulverize leaves, branches and tough stems into much smaller pieces for compost. Lay this around whatever you already have growing, adding seaweed mulch if you can; and make sure that air can circulate, so don't pack it down too hard. Try to analyse the main content of your soil. Clay? Chalky? Gravelly? Each type will have its preferences. In any case, seaweedy compounds will help. Remember that the polders, those large areas of land reclaimed from the North Sea off Holland, are beds for some of the world's loveliest flowers and have produced grazing land for some of the cattle which produce cheeses, butter and other dairy foods which many feel are second to none.

Different soils achieve different results and I must refer you, in this introduction, to rich alluvial soil over gravel subsoil if you are planning to grow good things in your back garden, let alone if you are seriously considering entering the business of market gardening! In Britain there are certain organizations which may prove helpful to both the aspirant professional grower and the concerned domestic gardener. The Soil Association, now based in Bristol, is unfailingly helpful and reliable with enquiries, as are the Organic Growers' Association and the Biodynamics Association. A brief word of warning here – and the associations mentioned above will be able to advise – many manufacturers market products that claim to be organically grown: if in doubt dowse the goods or buy only if you see the Soil Association's or Biodynamics' symbol on the label. Other claims should be read with circumspection if not suspicion . . . I have mixed feelings about how organic growing is becoming big business now. On the whole you can trust the claims of the large and reputable supermarket chains: they have too much to lose if their promises are not kept, as public awareness of the need for organic food increases. The day will certainly come, and soon, when people won't feel embarrassed about dowsing in a supermarket, but in the meantime I think that the large supermarkets are setting a good organic example in many areas.

Nonetheless, be careful when you choose tinned things. Anchovies, mackerel and sardines should be all right so long as the can isn't aluminium, but I'm wary of all frozen foods. Human beings were not designed to be the same size and to fit neatly into weight-monitored packets: nor were garden peas, carrots or sprouts. I suggest you consider buying instead the knobbly, 'dirty' unevenly shaped and sized ones you might buy elsewhere and resign yourself to all of three minutes washing or scraping them.

We live in a 'fast food' culture. But there are such things as expensive economies and dangerous, damaging 'short cuts'. If you think you're too tired to peel a carrot or chop an onion it might be worth considering whether your diminished energy is connected to the paucity of the nutrition in the food you bought so expensively in the local supermarket. You may have saved a few minutes, but how insignificant will that time seem when you are laid off work for a week or more because your body systems have not been up to strength?

Here, then, is a very short list of good things that anyone with a garden or even a grow-bag or window box can grow at home: Tom Thumb lettuce, dandelion leaves, spring onions, chives and other herbs, cherry tomatoes, garlic, sorrel and cresses. If you have only the tiniest outdoor wall space you can train honeysuckle for teas and tinctures. Mint will love to hug the base of that wall, as will lavender and lemon thyme. If you have only a little more space study the catalogues, and plant seeds for dwarf beans and other vegetables. Only an extra few yards will have you raising potatoes and runner beans – remember that herbs and vegetables can be as fragrant and decorative as they grow as flowers and shrubs. Also remember that an indoor (regularly emptied) compost bucket or bin is as useful to the flat-dweller as the garden heap for those with a proper garden. Good fruit and vegetable peelings should never be wasted . . .

The dangers of eating foods 'cleansed' with insecticides whilst growing was brought horribly and clearly home to me by the plight of seventy-three-year-old ME.

ME came to me two weeks after he had been diagnosed as

having cancer of the colon and concerned about the surgery planned for a few weeks after that.

Upon examining him I found that there were several gaps in his aura, but my pendulum guided me towards his abdomen nonetheless, and I discovered that his levels of essential levels of copper and silica were alarmingly low. Further dowsing indicated that the colon cancer had been caused by a problem in the right lung where asbestos particles had been trapped due to these deficiencies. I ascertained this by measuring the levels of the element germanium in the lung and remained convinced that this problem was the primary source of his condition; his colon was simply responding in a secondary 'knock-on' way. This domino effect of illness, particularly where damaged cells in one part of the body can announce their presence in quite another, is both frightening and all too common.

The lack of aura in the abdomen was caused by a genetic deficiency well over 3,000 years old and I set about dealing with that. But I also found that my patient's current problems related to a jamming of the pyloric valve which connects the stomach and the duodenum and that this blockage was caused by DDT, a pesticide.

It seemed that he had aggravated his condition by taking indigestion tablets to counter the stomach problems he'd suffered after consuming foods contaminated by DDT. This may have been the apparent cause of his cancer but the illness and his inability to deal with it naturally were rooted in those lung problems. Within ten minutes of applying a remedy to restore his missing aura his germanium levels rose dramatically and

I was able to set about removing asbestos from his lung.
If this can be cleared the colon may be able to correct
itself – this will take time but the trauma of surgery may
be avoided or at least delayed until he is much stronger
and better able to recover from it.

ME's example illustrates how a pesticide, inadvertently taken,
can activate a serious illness down the line and apparently
unrelated to the obvious area of illness. It also shows how every
system of our body – which was designed to be in perfect
balance – can be placed out of kilter by a fault on a connecting
meridian far from the apparent root of an illness. Remember,
pesticides can kill.

Other culprits lurk in bathroom cupboards and bedrooms. It
is important to remember that organic awareness is not confined
to dangers from foodstuffs. Over and over again I have dowsed
patients to find that cosmetics, nylon and other synthetics, even
such 'innocent' items as tissues, tampons and other cotton items
associated with health and cleanliness, are loaded with negative
chemical poisons and potentially harmful. Don't be misled by the
white box, the clinical packaging. Think and dowse before you
buy and use.

In an ideal world we would all wear cotton, silk, linen and
pure wool and only eat and drink uncontaminated things. We
would have immaculate homes and breathe perfect air and have
limitless time to pursue this ideal life. I'm well aware that few of
us can aspire to such perfection and so merely hope to suggest
here some easy guidelines. Cotton usually costs a little more than
polyester, whether for bedlinen or underwear, but it is cheap at
the price. The pressure points of a nylon bra affect the pancreas.

Lycra can also be damaging. Stick to cotton and your pancreas will thank you.

It may be attractive to have thick lashes but if the mascara affects your eyesight it is a very expensive luxury.

Think again before reaching for any old advertised shampoo. If your hair seems greasy it may be because your liver is having trouble emulsifying internal fats. Perhaps you have dandruff? Washing your hair again won't solve that problem: consider the liver, dowse it, ask it the questions about diet. The answers given may well solve more than the problem of greasy hair: they might give guidance towards the resolution of a more serious internal problem.

Many of my patients suffer from dioxin poison, a chemical used to make textiles and other materials whiter than white. Dioxin can creep into the uterus from the regular use of tampons and bleached tea bags should never be used because of their dioxin content. In fact the substance I use to remove dioxin from the system is obtained from empty tea bags soaked in alcohol which gives me enough for my like with like extraction purposes – a safer way of dealing with internal toxins. For instance, I had a patient who was seriously ill with an acute iron deficiency. I dowsed and discovered that he was suffering from severe lead poisoning. Dowsing showed that the times when he had absorbed lead coincided with times when he was at home, part of a large old house which still had a lead water tank. During his second session with me I extracted his lead poisoning and this slowly released the hitherto locked-up iron he needed. I used metals heavier than lead on the atomic scale in homeopathic form – like with like again. Not surprisingly my patient had also consulted his usual doctor about his low energy condition. The good man quickly diagnosed an extreme iron deficiency and gave my patient an iron injection. Perhaps because of the fluid 'carrier' in the syringe the patient died within two days.

Even rubber car tyres can release negative energies and enzymes, poisons which we all breathe in every time we walk along the road. But awareness can lead to protection.

We live in an unsafe world. Any one of us could be injured in some unforeseen accident, healthy as we might be. But it is within our power to minimize the risks of serious hurt, damage or illness.

Always remember that your body is not simply linked together by bones and tubes and a covering of skin. Essential though these are, the meridian lines which inform each separate part, muscle, bone and cell are also connected. And they depend on what you put in and what you take out – whether you feel unwell or not. Whether you need the advice of a specialist like me or not. Those facial laughter lines are signs of life, not decay. So are the little traces around the mouth or eyes. Bags under the eyes and things like cellulite may be at least partially due to inherited tendencies, but as I'm not a beautician I seldom worry about them (or encourage my patient to), unless they are signals of some avoidable diminishment of the life force.

Feeling tired, listless, stiff, nauseous, anxious or painful is another matter, however, and there is much that an organic diet can do to offer fast relief and, as a by-product, take years off your face, spirit and body . . .

Some of the chemicals used for years in tanning lotions, hair conditioners and colourants have a direct effect on a woman's reproductive system. This can be corrected, but the earlier use of such products is stopped the better. If menstrual discomfort has been experienced this will probably be lessened and another damaging circle broken – fewer tensions, a reduced dependency on painkilling drugs. These invariably create their own sub-symptoms and, with the loss of the natural magnetic aura, call for or demand more synthetic drugs . . . and so the downward spiral twists. It is part of my work to reverse that spiral and turn it both down to the soil and up to the sea and the light – naturally.

It is up to the individual to take stock and decide what matters most to them and to their family, if they have one. Perhaps changes must be made, sacrifices, even. The small sacrifice, for instance, of spending five minutes longer in the kitchen or market, of giving up a favourite lotion or shampoo in the name and hope of organic health. It takes a flying leap of faith to refuse penicillin or other drugs, and to believe in the body's ability to heal itself.

And of course we have the right to expect a cabbage without caterpillars, a lettuce without slugs, a rose without greenfly, and taste, fragrance, well-being and health as seldom before experienced. It now all seems so simple to me. It will work that way for you, too.

CHAPTER NINE

Homeopathy and Holistics

Why should we fear growing older? A good age should be something to be eagerly anticipated rather than dreaded. There will be more time to read those books you always meant to, learn a new language, travel, enjoy a saner pace of life, see and listen to your family and friends. More money, too, enables us to pursue interests and activities that may well have been hurried or set aside when domestic and professional demands just had to be answered first. A good age should be just that – life's prime time.

Other civilizations and societies revered their elders for their wisdom, experience and mellowed decency. But in Britain and much of the West today old age is more often associated with a kind of pinched pessimism, physical and mental deprivation, a morbid wish to die. It must be said that many elderly people with fixed ideas about how things were 'in their day' and an unrealistic, rosy memory of a better past (which was probably pretty awful, actually), do sometimes have themselves to blame for some of the impatience that is directed at them.

It doesn't have to be like that. Older people are often disagreeable and cantankerous because they are in pain, or feel undervalued, misunderstood or guilty about being a drain on family or social resources. Were they vital, lively, independent and useful members of their family or community they would not be patronized or even merely tolerated, pitied or despised. Rather, as they vigorously maintain their health and interests, their contributions would be welcomed and respected, and they would actually be *expected* to get on with their own, full lives – their knowledge and experience respected when not peevishly demanded.

Lord Malmesbury arrived at my clinic with a condition known as farmer's lung. This might sound like some amusing Restoration comedy joke, such as gout, but like gout it is no fun at all. Without inhalers he struggled for breath, and he had suffered from asthma since his fifties. He had been diagnosed with a lung disease resulting from sensitization to a fungus in mouldy hay. I knew by dowsing that he had mould in his lung which I cleared with a remedy made from ergot. He was also suffering from toxins in the steroids prescribed for his asthma. Tablets to extract these blockages were applied and a year later Lord Malmesbury has all but thrown away his sticks and can enjoy increasingly long, healthy walks with his dogs, breathing fresh country air without fear or difficulty. No longer does he need help to get out of his bath. Three main factors contributed to Lord Malmesbury's improvement: his spirit and faith, the care of his wife and, I guess, the treatments that I recommended. He looks forward to a great celebration on his ninetieth birthday. It was very encouraging anyway, I thought, that a man of his age should have the pluck and the will to get better rather than to give up and sink into some cosseted but uncomfortable dotage. I always admire spirit like that.

This is another of the areas where my homeopathic and holistic approach to healing plays a very important part. Eternal life does not seem to me to be, in itself, a particularly desirable goal, although some may misinterpret my ideas here: remember what I said about the beauty and health of a tree. It will weather and branch ever more majestically until its time is up. Then it will die, gracefully sink, and return to the soil which nourished its birth and growth so long ago. The human cycle need be no different.

Homeopathy and its close cousin, holistic healing, can help to achieve and echo this proper budding, flowering and strong maturity of a full lifespan.

MD was seventy-two and not enjoying his retirement.
He had almost given up, what with muscular weakness, a threat of glaucoma and dreadful breathlessness. For him the deterioration of memory and other mental powers was worse than the stiffness and gout. After dowsing I found that he had a patch of aluminium toxin in his right temple – something quite often found in patients suffering from Alzheimer's disease. I learned that he had worked with aluminium as an apprentice in the aircraft industry.

After ten visits and treatments his improvement is startling: memory function is better and general health much restored after I corrected fifteen faults in his aura. Firstly he was very curious when he visited – to the point that I might have wondered if he was sceptical – and wanted to know every detail of the treatments I was suggesting. I took this to be a sign of returning strength, and was pleased, as it indicated a sharpening of the memory processes. Now I know that any reservations he might once have had about the clinic are gone. Upon leaving he always asks about the next appointment: no one does this without trust, faith and hope and these days, I believe, he has good reasons to hope for a very fulfilled future.

Genetic science, so pivotal to my work and ideas, is a ruthless dictator. Weakened or flawed genes will, in the reproductive process over generations within any family, become weaker and even more flawed. Sometimes I feel like a King Canute in attempting to arrest this tide, but with careful dowsing it can be done, enabling each new generation to set off in life with a clean genetic slate. Whilst these beliefs may seem to apply mainly to our newly born, they are in fact inextricably liked to older members of the community.

People who worry about the burden placed on state and society by a population of elderly spongers should remember that healthy elders will not drain hospital resources, may well want to work far beyond the conventional pensionable age and have much more to offer society than they take from it. Healthy elders will not need hip replacements, heart surgery or special housing. I tried to refuse to accept my old age pension some years ago, telling the authorities that I'd like to start claiming when I was eighty. My request was denied. I didn't feel 'past it' at sixty-five or seventy or even at eighty, and nor need anyone else. It insults older people to treat them like dependent babies and it is time that all our youth-culture ideas and ideals are revised. Attitudes which tend to treat old age as a sin or imposition, rather than something to be quietly respected and admired, should be reconsidered. So I don't endorse special congratulations for someone who is fit and active at eighty or ninety, as if this was something extraordinary . . . Our

Western civilization is not so very ancient and wise. It may pay to study and remember the attitudes of older societies' attitudes to health and age.

I'm as pleased to help an older person make the most of the last half or third of their life as I am to relieve the suffering of a child or lift the nicotine poisoning from the lungs of an adult.

BP has been a patient since she was sixty. Back in 1986 she decided to see me about her high blood pressure, severe hip pains and groin pain rather than take the drugs her doctor had prescribed. Eleven years on, her hip maintains the improvement I had achieved through homeopathic treatments but recently her blood pressure and cholesterol levels have crept up. With knowledge that I have acquired since first seeing her I dowsed her system and found that the DNA controlling her abdominal muscles was jammed with tannin poison which was blocking her zinc supply, and this in turn was affecting her heart.

Four weeks later her blood pressure had dropped dramatically and her cholesterol level was almost normal. She was again enjoying much of the limber agility that enables her to play with and look after her grandchildren. But she is still not quite well yet and she deserves many more years of good health, so I was still worried about the residual pain in her lower back.

During her most recent visit I discovered, through dowsing, that she suffered from poor absorption of vitamin B_6, possibly contributing to her lower back pains and certainly causing nervous reactions, particularly to sudden noises. Her B_6 blockage was caused by ergot poisoning, acquired whilst she was in her mother's womb. The body's distributing point for all vitamins is situated in the left lower bowel and she admitted that she had always experienced some discomfort in this area. After treatments this blockage, too, was removed and the pain lifted. We must wait and see, but as I write her condition improves – years after her doctors had all but given up.

Then there is the case of young HC, born with a heart murmur, constantly unwell since birth – with asthma amongst other things. Much current medical thinking – whilst not exactly dismissing the importance of such conditions – tends to throw its hands up in despair and regard them as the bad luck of the draw or 'just one of those things'. I part company with this thinking here: it doesn't have to be like that, and a study of a patient's DNA and their family tree will often get to the root of a problem and suggest remedies

Some time after I treated HC he was checked at the famous and distinguished Guy's Hospital, where it was found that the hole in his heart was so small that it had all but closed up. His asthma, too, had cleared. But all was not yet completely well. When I saw him two years later he was three-and-a-half and showing signs of dyslexia and autism. His distraught parents had been told by a Berkshire hospital that there was little hope of any improvement.

Six months later and after eleven further visits to me he is much improved: he has a growing vocabulary, makes eye contact as he could not before, does not fall over all the time now that his spinal cord is strengthened and

plays with learning toys in a very constructive way.
Perhaps he will never be an Olympic athlete or a great
intellectual, but he will achieve his potential nonetheless.
His parents are naturally delighted and relieved.

I mention these two examples – that of a child and that of an
elderly patient – to show what can be achieved: it isn't always total
relief but it is often an improvement hitherto believed
unimaginable.

As far as I know the first physician who recorded the importance
of a holistic approach to medicine was the German physician
Samuel Hahnemann, working in a small Prussian community in
the late eighteenth and early nineteenth centuries. His patients
tended to stay in their villages, generation after generation, and he
was thus able to observe similar ailments replicated over as many
as four generations in the same family. In his day almost all
medicine was plant- and herb-based, and during a lifetime's
study, work and application he could see how many problems
could be reduced. He saw that a grandfather's ailment need not
still be evident two or three generations later.

Hahnemann understood the importance of nature's magnetic
fields. He also recognized how these can become blocked by
miasmas of disease and how they sometimes connected with a new
patient's disorder. His pioneering notes remain essential to any
study of the science of homeopathy. He recognized the body's
capacity for healing itself and introduced the idea of treating *like
with like* by applying carefully devised homeopathic tablets to a
patient's tongue. He was aware that in this way he could activate the
body's hitherto closed immune system. The homeopathic approach

to disease is to help the body acquire its own immunity and help itself – no damage can be done to the basic human DNA blueprint.

A contemporary of Hahnemann, the British scientist Edward Jenner, was also pursuing strands of similar ideas. In his day Jenner revolutionized current medical thinking about disease by injecting a tiny strain of the 'cow pox' virus into humans, thus simultaneously reducing the spread of smallpox and establishing the principles of vaccination. So impressed was Queen Victoria that she insisted upon all her children being inoculated. Jenner pioneered what I call 'passive immunity'.

Contemporary civil engineers laid pipes to take away sewage in nineteenth-century town gutters but gained little credit for the clean water and reduction in the instances of bacterial disease that followed. The understanding of how to acquire natural immunity was still a long way off but Jenner should be acknowledged as another pioneer, even if his principles have sometimes been traduced.

Parents bring babies and children with a wide range of problems to me. Tragically, I find that the DNA of these youngsters is often at great variance with the body's 'master plan'. Lungs which are short of the complicated DNA instructions which we all need do not function properly, and it has been proved that often not only is this defect inherited but it also becomes worse over succeeding generations. A parent who needs one inhaler to breathe properly will produce children who need two. We all know that our DNA should function like a well-oiled machine: jam that machine with vaccines and the entire efficiency of the human reproductive processes will eventually fail.

Little BC had been born normally; both his mother and grandmother had been my patients, so I knew quite a lot

about the family health history and I knew that there was
a strain of TB there. I strongly advised that BC should
not be vaccinated but his mother wavered under medical
pressure and bullying and at the age of six weeks he had
his first vaccination. Within days he was brought to me in
a plastic tent, being kept alive with steroids. It wasn't,
mercifully, too late for me to extract much of the poison
and his mother stonewalled all further attempts to make
her give consent for other jabs. Ben is now a thriving,
healthy five-year-old and I believe his mother's
determination to spare him more vaccinations has
certainly saved him from a life of ill health.

BF is a sixty-six-year-old pharmacist, one of the breed
who still dispense herbs and other non-chemical
remedies. He became worried about a series of
abdominal pains and a hard swelling there. By dowsing I
found that both his left and right frontal skull areas
contained impurities which were seriously damaging
function. As this part of the brain controls the working
instructions for the abdomen I reasoned that the root of
the pains lay there.

Further dowsing revealed that he had been given a BCG
TB test when he was twenty-two and drafted into the army.
Forty-four years later the substance used for that test had
spread to his brain and was preventing him from absorbing
inositol, PABA and silica. These three control or affect,
respectively, fat globules, lymph drainage and the nerves.

I placed a pad of homeopathic tablets, devised
especially for this condition, on his frontal skull. Their

power of extraction is immense. He left the surgery
without pain and his abdomen had softened impressively.

In Hahnemann's work a patient was likely to recover if prescribed minute but strong plant or herbal extractions of the essential force of the strain which controlled the illness. He made the body fight back. Without today's 'isms' and parroted formulae Hahnemann understood and recorded how cells could be distorted and damaged over generations – in short, some of the basic principles of DNA. With his understanding of the threads of illness that linked children to their grandparents he established – and almost legitimized – a notion that most people take for granted today: that one does not inherit merely a certain jawline or colouring but can also be blessed with a noble brow or saddled with a tendency to specific illness. He discovered by trial and error how these could be corrected. Sleeping time bombs such as inherited venereal disease, TB and diphtheria were eventually conquered or controlled thanks to his findings and his little sugar-based pills placed on the patient's tongue. We are all indebted to him, the father of homeopathy. Hahnemann understood that each body had a magnetic field which could tell a physician much more about the health of the patient than their temperature or pulse rate might.

Never underestimate the power of your brain. It controls everything else in your body, including your skin. The body will respond to all its messages and a brain fed with negative thoughts will react in a negative way somewhere in the system. This isn't to suggest that we should all be permanent Pollyannas and never worry, fret or even rage from time to time: we are only human.

But we are all capable of consciously balancing things, at least seeking some harmony, so that the brain can send positive as well as negative messages. It is, after all, our controller, it knows everything and affects everything.

It's infuriating when others say 'cheer up' or 'don't worry' or 'don't let it get you down' as if such changes of mindset can be easily willed. They can't, but there is some wisdom in both the prosaic 'look on the bright side' and the profound advice once suggested by a courtier to an ancient Chinese emperor. 'This, too, will pass' is a useful and sane phrase to remember during both the highs and lows of life.

The idea rather echoes the centuries-later sentiments of Rudyard Kipling in his poem 'If', in which he counselled that those 'two impostors' triumph and disaster should be looked at coolly and not allowed to control. If you consider these statements they do both embody a holistic attitude to mental and physical health: the essential sense of sanity and balance. Fears and negative thoughts really do create 'bad vibrations' which the brain sends out to every part of the body. I try to help to restore balance to my patient's brain, to curb those destructive vibrations.

Do not misunderstand: the fact that I lay great stress on the brain's functions is not to suggest that I regard every patient as mentally unwell. Far from it. But I absolutely believe that physical health cannot be separated from the neurological. The brain is also a heavy physical thing – weighing as much as your arm – and is your most crucial, strong yet delicate possession.

And heartless as this may seem to some readers, I'm a student of the 'it's not my problem' school of thought. If other people have brought their burdens and angers to your doorstep – so much so that you have taken on their worries, hatreds and guilts to the extent that you can no longer quite distinguish between their concerns and your own – cut loose, especially if you feel that you have enough on your own plate already. Be fair to yourself and your brain.

Concentrate all your positive healing forces on yourself and after that you may well be better placed to offer support to your distressed friend or relative. In the end 'looking after number one' benefits everyone, however hard or heartless the initial decision to do so might seem to be. Your body already has its work cut out: a weakened system may be further troubled by the load of other people's and this helps no one. Strive for detachment.

Aggressions, both your own and those that others might have burdened you with, can easily activate the brain's neurons, spread through the body and damage all its functions. It's enough to take on and attempt to deflect all the everyday risks and hidden poisons which affect us all every time we merely walk down the street. It is only rational: take care of yourself; only then may you be able to help others.

Returning to practical things, I am sometimes asked if medicines and creams, pills and other treatments sold to the public as 'homeopathic' are safe. The items sold by a well-known, long-established and reputable homeopathic chemist, both in their London shop and in other outlets, are in the main admirable. Remember, however, that some other less reliable high street chemists and chains may have jumped on a fashionable bandwagon and be a little less careful about labelling their wares. However high the quality of the remedies, if the package has to be passed through an electronic till after you have chosen your purchases, the bar code may simply record some sugar-based product. So be careful if you buy coded 'homeopathic' remedies.

I must warn against anything that contains lanolin, a sheep-derived substance which may include organophosphate pesticides. This can be especially dangerous for babies, and it is ironic that many products sold as emollients for infant rashes etc. contain lanolin. Avoid products, also, containing petroleum and never use such products on a baby. You may be confident that almond oil is a safe ingredient.

Choose carefully and buy wisely. Always read the label on the tube or box and if a list of constituents isn't given don't even consider buying it. Certainly never place it anywhere near your head or that of anyone else's as the crown is especially receptive to dangerous substances and the use of lanolin-based products here could counter and block the good work that other treatments may be trying to achieve in eliminating fungi or blockages inside the body.

Such 'cures' can actually prevent the body's own pretty wonderful cleansing or immune systems of acids, saliva, and fungal bacteria-fighters from doing their jobs in helping the body to deflect or deal with the knock-out blow.

Holistic medicine and regimes have become quite fashionable in recent years and whilst I applaud the spread of the holistic approach I have to offer a short warning about signing on for a course of treatments that may prove to be so costly that worry about meeting the bills could cause some new problems. Holistic treatment often requires the separate attentions of an acupuncturist, reflexologist, chiropractor, herbalist and any number of other specialists, working together though they are. With respect to each of these redoubtable healers, this approach reminds me sometimes of that of conventional medicine wherein a patient is shunted from specialist to specialist, ward to ward, as separate aspects of their illness are dealt with in turn. Few people visiting a holistic healer can expect – ironically, given the 'wholeness' of any person upon which holistic principles are based – to be seen by just one healer who eventually understands the entirety of the person in their care.

I repeat that I never promise miracles, but I do try – and often succeed – to treat every aspect of a patient's problem. They may have to wait three weeks or more to get an appointment (unless there is an emergency to deal with), but after that there is, literally, a one to one relationship between patient and healer. These days my iridologist colleague will have helped me to begin by analysing my patient's eyes and if they wish to accept the separate therapy she can offer it is their choice. But I am willing to deal with all their problems and don't feel the need to refer them elsewhere. An understanding of all the body's interconnecting meridians enables a healer like me to address and treat virtually every aspect of an illness.

Some of the homeopathic tablets I prepare for patients are devised to draw out toxins, others to release energies, both working through the pores of the skin. I have made careful tests with a magnetometer, weighing the pills after they have been removed from the skin. Those which extracted toxins from the body were heavier than they were before and those which released energy were lighter. Some particularly complex tests, undertaken with Tony Pagdin, who is distinguished in many scientific fields, involved fruit flies in sealed glass jars. Some of the jars contained tablets imbued with extracted toxins and others didn't. The insects in the jars containing 'used' tablets all died whilst the others lived.

Another time we observed the behaviour of some benign bacterial growth placed near both used and unused homeopathic tablets. The used tablets inhibited the growth of the bacteria.

Some bacteria are helpful but antibiotics such as penicillin can be dangerous and homeopathic tablets potented with extracted antibiotics can prevent the spread of harmful cultures.

Controlled experiments such as these convince me, almost as much as the observation of recovery, that my methods are working.

All over the country there are people who work in my way. That some have been trained here at my clinic gives me pride, but that many others have been embracing the same principles as me and are spreading the ideas which we all share gives me even greater pleasure.

It is never too late to arrest illness and never too late to learn. Three years ago I feared that I couldn't help my sister-in-law after her stroke. She was immobile, incapable of speech and we both despaired. But plants I dowsed in Malta have reversed much of this and she is now active and talks quite coherently. The subtext of this message is: *Be positive. Never give up.*

I called the herbs that I found in Malta, after my pendulum had guided me there, Formula 525. I placed a small pad of these blended herbs on the pulse of her right hand, allowing a controlled charge of their healing energy to reach her heart. My sister-in-law was very patient and as well as accepting my treatment she had therapy at a remedial stroke group at her local hospital. Her progress is slow but steady and I have faith that eventually a near-total recovery from her stroke can be achieved.

I have never understood why babies should be washed immediately after their birth. Even worse is when they are dabbed with even a mild disinfectant such as hypochlorite, phenols compounds, quaternary or ammonium within their first twenty-four hours: it leaves me speechless. I'm afraid I often find, in my searchings and dowsings, that patients have tell-tale blockages and patches in their systems as a result of such chemical measures when they were babies. Any substance applied to a new baby's skin will affect them for life and the 'nasties' can prevent the formation of the skin's magnetic fields. Without this force the skin and bones cannot function correctly and a lifetime of damaged health and reduced potential will certainly follow.

A particular challenge comes from patients who have inherited a gene which prevents them from feeling pain. In extreme cases these people have no reaction to walking on splintered glass, excruciating dental treatments, dangerous burns or bone fractures. Some of them take a misguided pride in their 'fortitude' and their 'high pain threshold', without understanding that pain is our friend, alerting us to conditions that beg urgent attention. A general feeling of being slightly unwell is often all they will admit to. These patients are tough nuts – but as they never admit or 'submit', they seldom, either, feel alive. Dangerous symptoms of life-threatening maladies can thus be superficially masked simply because some misguided mindset has refused to allow them to acknowledge their pain.

I've been able to treat several such patients. An inability to experience pain is often demonstrated by the lack of response to the harmless pressure of a sharp point being gently applied to the skin on the back of their hand. Almost always here my dowsing has revealed a birth defect.

There might be a blockage in their atlas (the first cervical vertebra) caused by the pethidine painkiller administered in an epidural to their mother during their birth. Any lumbar treatment by pethidine can cause much future distress for the child. I release such blockages by treatment applied to points on the back of the neck where nerves and parts of the sensory system are located.

There is some truth in the familiar, almost clichéd warnings concerning 'the sins of the fathers'. With the very best of intentions, your grandparents may have insisted on all the new vaccinations for their children, not knowing that those toxins could be passed down to you. Your illness today could well connect with blockages caused by such pollutants, but don't despair: the toxins can be removed and replaced by mending, healing elements which will restore balance and health.

One of my patients, a young man, was horribly debilitated by depression. I dowsed and learned that his mother had attempted to abort with pills prescribed by her GP when her pregnancy was fairly well advanced. This young man had been permanently affected in the womb by both his mother's worries and the chemicals which 'nourished' him during her pregnancy. I was able to extract the poisons which had blighted his life for so long.

'I feel better,' he told me when his treatments were completed. These three words are the sweetest ones I can ever hope to hear.

CHAPTER TEN

A Working Day

L et us say that someone comes to me with a skin condition like psoriasis (unsightly, itchy, crusty with flaking patches all over the body), or with such constant pain in their neck, shoulders and upper back that they are rarely comfortable and have been unable to sleep well for months, which in itself will probably have triggered further strains and problems. Perhaps a patient complains of a general decline in energy and life force or *joie de vivre*. The chances are that each of these patients is further depressed by repeated failure of treatments prescribed by other practitioners, and they may, furthermore, feel baffled, because they believe they have done all they could to eat sensibly and have followed their doctor's orders to the letter. It's a downward spiral: how can I try to reverse it?

Obviously we talk and I try to learn about their medical history and records, what drugs they have been prescribed, and so on. I often think that it's a little ironic that my work has required me to become something of an expert on the properties of the commercially produced drugs I so deplore. But I need to understand how they 'work' before I can devise an antidote with which to extract drug residue from a patient's system. Sad to say, my knowledge in this field is ever widening and my shelves ever more crammed with antidotes as more and more damaging drugs are routinely prescribed.

I'm interested to know about the health patterns, if any, within their family. I do my mercury check, take those clippings of hair and nail and proceed to do my best. Some people need just one consultation with me to have that spiral reversed upwards, others take many more sessions, but with faith and confidence on both sides I can often help.

My patients divide about fifty/fifty between those with physical and those with mental or emotional troubles.

Recently I saw DE, a young girl from Wales who having been healthy and even athletic until recently was now so depressed and traumatized by bullying at school that she couldn't face her classroom. That she was exceptionally bright and pretty was probably part of the problem – her bullies were jealous of her. Fond parental advice and reassurance hadn't worked: the girl remained too frightened to face her tormentors.

I was able to locate the source of this as being a trauma that prevented her from absorbing protein; without it her otherwise strong DNA could not function and was not resilient enough to cope with her bullies. With the application of tablets containing both Mercoam and appropriate gene extracts from Welsh trees on her wrists, the blockage was loosened and released and she quickly recovered much of her strength and courage.

I also found that an ear infection she had suffered as a baby had been treated with antibiotics which gradually eroded the lining of her oesophagus long after the ear infection had cleared. Indigestion and bowel problems followed. The antibiotics had caused a blockage in the essential silica supply to the brain and this deficiency affected the nerve which would have enabled her to survive the psychological onslaught of the bullying. It's almost a miracle that she had been able to do so well on the playing field despite all this – perhaps it was because here she was away from her classroom and playground adversaries. Crystals from six separate bottled solutions removed the old trauma and I took the residual antibiotics out of her system by the application of tablets to her throat. She told me during her treatment that she could feel her body tingling as her toxins were removed. Soon, almost at once, she was able to face school again and dismiss with confidence the cowardly spite of the tormentors. Her grandmother telephoned me to confirm this happy advance – she has a new group of friends and her schoolwork is excellent again.

Perhaps because it accounts for more working days lost each year in Britain than any other ailment, nothing makes people mutter about malingerers more than back pain. But a back which is out of kilter in any one of a number of places can not only cause excruciating pain and be truly debilitating but can place the rest of the body under severe stress. Think of an old-fashioned tent with a damaged ridge pole: it will sag at best and collapse at worst.

EF had suffered from various allergies for most of her life and from muscular weakness and a painful back for a year before she visited me. Pain was upsetting her sleep and nothing – fasting, consultations with various doctors and healers, physiotherapy and two scans – had helped to ease her terrible 'bone-cracking' pain. She could barely walk. But after three visits to my clinic she was sleeping normally and her pain had gone. So too were her swollen glands, hot flushes, sore throat and stiff neck and shoulders.

The simple reason for her daunting list of ailments was poison in her system absorbed through suntan lotion. I extracted the toxin from where it had lodged at the base of her spine (the sacroiliac) and she now has energy she did not believe she could ever possess again.

Another patient, BB, had a severe back problem too. Despite hospital blood tests and X-rays, and years of osteopathic treatment, he needed to wear a support belt and still could not lift anything or even raise his arms above his shoulders. He wasn't yet sixty-four years old.

Eventually he was brought to me by his brother, whom I had successfully treated five years earlier, but not before he had overcome a good deal of cynical prejudice. Within minutes I could tell that BB's parathyroid was so weak that he could not absorb calcium or vitamin D and these deficiencies were causing bone stress and thus the pain. With just two of the appropriate tablets taped into place Bill's pain lifted within two minutes – and, to his astonished delight, he could raise his arms, too. Next the body belt was discarded and Bill could rise from a crouching position without effort or pain. The brothers left for their 150 mile car journey home without dread of the discomfort that Bill had endured on the way to my clinic. Obviously I wish that all my treatments showed such fast and demonstrably satisfactory results.

One patient, CD, reckoned that over the last seventeen years he had been prescribed and taken over 100,000 tranquillizers. Doctor after doctor had attempted to address his symptoms rather than the causes of his disability.

I don't wholly condemn this, realizing that GPs are usually busy people who often have to deal with malingerers. A quick prescription of some placebo pill may well enable them to give the time, care and understanding that other patients need. CD, however, was unlucky in that for many years he was fobbed off with prescriptions for depression and a severe mental collapse. These treatments only served to aggravate his problems. His thriving business failed, his wife returned to Holland with their children and in his drug-dazed and hazy state he was quite incapable of fighting back. He was surviving on diminishing savings in a supervised centre, far away from residual friends and family. But CD had a doctor in the Midlands who heard about my work and persuaded him to brave the journey to see me.

I was shocked when I met him. He didn't look older than his sixty-odd years: he was tall, lean, actually rather handsome and clear of eye and skin. But he shivered and quivered like an epileptic, his speech was slow and vague even as he dramatically recalled aspects of his misfortunes, his hearing seemed damaged and he showed no hope or life force in his eyes, voice or posture. His throat was very sore. He had travelled some distance, made the physical and financial effort to stay nearby for three days, so I knew I had real time to try and help him and that I owed him special attention. On the first day I touched his head and brow and dowsed.

The poisons left by all those tens of thousands of pills had completely shot his nerve centres and created a serious magnesium deficiency. Large pads of tablets had to be taped across his throat, chest and lower abdomen. I also dowsed to find nicotine poisoning inherited from a smoker father and these toxins had to be drawn out as well. But there was strength in those genes too – his grandmother had lived to be ninety-six and I was confident that I could restore to him that vital inherited DNA.

CD was candid about the events and conditions that led him to me.

'I had lost my life. My family and friends had all given up on me. My business was finished. Not surprising, really, when you consider that I once blew thousands of pounds on plastic bottles for cleaning and washing-up liquids although I no longer had a factory where they could be filled. So I had lost my mind as well.'

I found, in dowsing, that his ancestors had come from Surrey, so perhaps in some way that drew him to my clinic. He has genes from female ancestors who lived 7,000 years ago, at least one of whom lived to be well over 130. The male forebears lived even longer. Having dowsed for the patient's auras and learned something of his DNA, I made homeopathic tablets from distilled essence of wood from the healthy trees which are nourished by minute fragments of his ancestral remains. With this DNA memory diluted into tablets, I was able to make some progress, and once the chemical blockages were removed his body was able to absorb nutrients again.

The second time CD came to the clinic he was visibly less twitchy, much more coherent and calmer. I knew that many of the toxins had been removed as he stripped away the pads of tablets that had absorbed poison through his pores overnight. But I also knew that internal pollutants deriving from vaccines he received before National Service in the Far East as a young man had yet to be extracted. He was a fit man before that, when he was twenty-two, and I strove to restore him to that state. So there was more dowsing to help me see where the nicotine and vaccination blockages were located and more tablets to apply. By the third day, without claiming that he was a completely mended or happy man, I could see how much better he was, and so could he. I couldn't promise him a revival in his business career or family situation, but I bade farewell to a man with hope and strength which he had not felt for many years. Much was achieved in our three days but neither he, nor any other patient, should assume that complete recovery can always take place swiftly. He made a wonderful start, a step towards full recovery, but now, after twenty-five years of chemical dependency, progress towards full recovery will be gradual, if not slow.

But he is basically cleansed now and has a new will to deal with emotional demons as well as the physical ones. The doctors and social workers who are keen on the 'quick fix' of cheap happy pills do their patients and clients no favours: this is one reason why I was so pleased that his doctor in Leicester, Patrick Kingsley, referred him to me after careful research and consideration. At last an enlightened GP realized that sometimes conventional diagnosis can work in fruitful partnership with my methods. I hope and expect to work with doctors like Patrick Kingsley again – it will be to the immense benefit of many patients like David and will spare them the exhausting and demoralizing shunting from one specialist to another, each one finally throwing up their palms before prescribing yet another chemical panacea.

Just as a hydrangea in your garden needs iron from its soil to bloom as a brilliant dark pink or blue and without that mineral will be pallid or even merely a greenish white, the human body needs its soil nutrients.

We all need gold, for instance. I'm not speaking of rings and necklaces but of the minute traces of gold found in most soils, the earth in which the food we eat grows. As with the patient mentioned earlier who needed magnesium, lack of these trace elements can lead to the sort of depression which doctors often seek to relieve with drugs like lithium. These substances can be found more naturally in stones and rocks. It might well take me a dowsing trek to find it, but as always, a minute quantity of the right, identified, pulverized stone can be reactivated indefinitely.

Gold is found in the brain, glands and bones and we need it to retain mental and emotional stability, but some people are unable to absorb it. Gold is a heavy metal and if another, heavier metal such as impure mercury has leaked into the system – through poor dental work, for instance – gold's absorption is blocked. In such instances I will apply the like with like principle and tape Mercoam to a pulse point such as the wrist, thus drawing out the mercury interference and allowing gold to do its work.

Often an appointment arranged to deal with a specific physical problem will become almost conversational as I try to explain to my patient how I was able to locate the source of the condition and then outline my reasons for advising the appropriate treatment. And *because* of the holistic nature of my work it is seldom easy to separate one aspect of it from another, so reminders about careful diet will often follow, especially if a simple plant example helps the patient understand what I have prescribed for them.

Many vegetables, cauliflower especially, need molybdenum in the soil to grow well. Its absence in the soil will result in flabby, nutrition-free produce with twisted stems. An addition of molybdenum, found in seaweed extracts, to the soil will miraculously and almost immediately cause the stalk to unwind and ease the release of proper nutrients into the vegetable, making it organically firm and bursting with goodness. And that same deficiency which contorted the cauliflower can lead to eye problems, including cataracts, in humans, so we need our molybdenum too and should try to eat foods rich in it, such as dark green vegetables, liver and whole-grain cereals.

Even though it is hard to rescue poor soil, I have to boast that the fields around my clinic, once the site of my market-garden business, prove day after day and year after year that organic feeding of the soil – especially when nourished by seaweed-based compounds – pays dividends. I rarely water or fertilize this grassy area these days, but the lawns are always a verdant, brilliant green, however dry the summer has been. What I placed in the soil all those years ago is still doing its work in a way that no commercially produced and bagged product ever could.

You should also be aware that an apple, say, bought in the supermarket and looking rosy, firm and glossy, has probably been culled from a tree 'fertilized' by appalling chemicals. It will contain as few real nutrients as the 'perfect' baby carrots in the next plastic bag along the shelf. And you can forget about its vitamin C ... Don't fear the dirty appearance of organic fruits and vegetables: that soil is life-giving.

I'm delighted to note that even such an august newspaper as the *Sunday Times* now endorses these views. India Knight's weekly watchdog column, which tests, compares and reviews standard supermarket items such as pre-prepared meals, dairy produce and condiments, frequently stresses the superiority of foodstuffs which contain organically produced ingredients and urges both the customer and the supermarket chains to take note.

We can't live in a sanitized, idealized world. Sometimes you'll risk a handful of salted peanuts even if you've heard from me and others that they are packed with and coated by unfriendly fungi. Few of us live in perfect and correctly sterile environments and I'm not sure that many of us would wish to. But we can be alert and try to avoid everyday pollution. Every little helps, of course, and we can choose unleaded petrol, shop around for decent food and query the prescription of chemically-based drugs whenever we can. But if you have a raging headache and no salvia to hand you might still reach for the paracetamol.

Consider things in your own time, in peace and quiet, and learn to trust, experiment and believe that there is a better way. Step by step the poisons which have caused illness can be removed. Your unique magnetic field will tell you how to rid yourself of ancient and inherited problems if your body is taught how to listen. It may take time but it will be worth the wait. Be alert.

I hope my work combines Western and modern holistic practice with the wisdom of the ancients of China who understood so much about our bodies' meridians. I try to offer practical as well as purely theoretical or philosophical advice. Sometimes I'm asked about food poisoning. This watchfulness is wise and good. The fact is that after we pass the age of fifty our body's ability to produce bifidobacteria – a substance which enables beneficial bacteria to thrive in our guts – is reduced. These enzymes fight the effects of any dodgy foodstuffs which we may have innocently and accidentally consumed. Whilst antibiotics and steroids try to counter the symptoms of food poisoning, they also destroy the good, friendly bacteria. Much better to eat yoghurt-based foods and dishes which contain Jerusalem artichoke. Its properties do much to stabilize an upset bowel or stomach. And don't imagine that only meat and fish can cause food poisoning. Although poor hygiene and lax controls in slaughterhouses and markets cause terrible outbreaks, clean but badly grown and farmed fruit and vegetables can cause just as much distress. And it is well known that a diet frequently lacking in fresh fruit and vegetables and heavy on cakes and biscuits prevails in Scotland, where several recent outbreaks of food poisoning have occurred. Older people anywhere who rely on cheap and dubious supermarket sausage and cold meats should especially beware.

The greatest gift of growing older, oddly, is time. No rush hour and no professional pressures. Income may be reduced, of course, but there is time to shop carefully, cook sensibly and above all to grow and nurture organically – even if there is only a window box to cultivate. And people with relaxed schedules should rarely need to resort to the fast, furious and foolish use of a microwave oven. You *can* utilize your microwave, however: it's a marvellous way of sterilizing potting soil.

It's hard to get the balance right, I realize, but 60 per cent of our nutrition should come from fruit and vegetables. The benefits are soon seen and felt. Apart from anything else, good fresh food is usually cheaper. Olive oil of course is expensive but that superb taste is worth it and its use is positively beneficial, especially to your heart, unlike butter or lard.

Recently I was shocked to learn that cetain hospitals, which were triumphantly claiming that their standards of cleanliness had improved, were actually too clean – the unguents and antiseptics had killed off the bacteria which help to heal us. We need, desperately, some of the tiny organisms which thrive in the soil. Health and hygiene are business partners but we mustn't mistake shining, gleamy, scented surfaces for perfection.

Few humans are perfect in the way that many a tree, stone or plant can be. I'm not actually sure that perfection should even be striven for, as it is usually the paradox, the inconsistency, even the flaw, which makes a person lovable or interesting. All I seek to achieve is the very best that is possible for my patients' measurable physical and mental health, and I have the stones, trees, flowers, herbs, soil and my dowsing to thank for that.

Some patients are referred to me by enlightened complementary practitioners, such as Carol Caplin, a consultant in many areas of health and fitness. Sometimes I refer my patients to *her* – and others – if I have a good idea about treatments which will be complementary to mine, and effective.

Carol writes:

> The people who consult me are in all areas of business
> and all walks of life. There is not one particular type of
> person, just those who are really interested and very keen
> to be well and healthy and to take responsibility for
> themselves by not taking drugs and painkillers to deal
> with any problems . . . My first knowledge of Jack was
> when I had done as much as I could do to help myself but
> I still had problems with my digestion and skin and was
> very tired all the time. I came four years ago, regularly
> after that for about eighteen months, and have not looked
> back. Now I come once or twice a year, much as one goes
> to the dentist, and I'm in superb internal health.

It is gratifying to get such an endorsement from a fellow healer
and professional. Many of Carol's patients are well known in
public life, as are a good few of mine, but the care of no one
patient matters to me more than that of another and I'm sure all
alternative healers would agree.

Much good sense is spoken about drug abuse these days but
sometimes these remarks are centred upon addictions to heroin,
cocaine and the like. We mustn't forget that the 'innocently'
prescribed sedatives and tranquillizers like lithium, Prozac and
Valium can be every bit as damaging.

Think, however, of a pebble or a leaf. There is such healing
wisdom there. Take it. Use it.

CHAPTER ELEVEN

Iridology and Cellular Biology

A ll new parents gaze with wonder and pride at the eyes of their baby, blinking and glazed as they sometimes are. They might wonder if the bright, fearless blue of the newborn will change to become brown, hazel or green. This is marvellous and natural and so is the science of iridology – a way that specialists can 'read' the state of your health by analysing and interpreting the messages contained within the iris.

You may think that your eyes are blue, grey, green, hazel, amber or brown. Actually there are only two colours of eye – blue and brown – and any deepening of colour is a result of some hereditary imbalance, often influenced by ancient toxins. The blue eye is rare and pure – but, once again, I must stress that I have no time for Aryan notions of perfection: what an ancestor may have eaten thousands of years ago will determine our eye colour just as surely as does the colour of our parents' eyes.

The 'mixed eye' is the one which I see most commonly. The blue eye usually speaks of a stronger constitution than a mixed one. Even an apparently clear grey eye or a shining brown one is likely to be mixed, as the colour of the iris is affected by the state of our health. The trained iridologist I work with has mixed brown eyes but she tells me that her iris colour has lightened considerably since self-recognized problems and an altered diet followed iridology.

Neither bright blue or deep brown, most people's eyes reflect inherited strengths or weaknesses in every part and organ of their body and the reading of this incredible map is crucial to my work. The eyes also reveal points of mental and emotional stress, suggesting where the problem is rooted so that I can dowse for help. Recorded study of patients' eyes and changes therein provides me with me a valuable means of monitoring progress. Please remember that I am not addressing ideas of conventional beauty here – someone who is unwell may yet have startlingly lovely eyes – but ideas of health. And the eyes do have it: I can short-circuit many long and laborious processes, including preliminary dowsing simply by studying the iridology report of the eyes of a new patient and/or a specially taken and enlarged photograph of them.

Every illness or disorder a patient has ever endured is recorded in the minute threads and fibres that colour the eye, and iridology thus presents an invaluable historical record of each patient's strengths, weaknesses and tendencies. The right eye and the left tell their own specific stories, with information about the whole body stored in each.

My iridologist colleague, extraordinarily skilled, always photographs the eyes of any new patient. She is a trained reflexologist and healer as well. During her painless, hour-long examination she can accurately pinpoint the source of a patient's trouble.

Using a sophisticated but nonetheless conventional camera fitted with special lenses which enlarge pictures of the patients' irises, she analyses the pictures and reports back to me. Her findings almost always make it easier for me to eliminate irrelevant signals, to identify the source of the problem and then to dowse for healing.

Iridology seeks to identify and locate areas in the body where there is some blockage and healing is thus required. It is not in itself a science which claims to help failing eyesight or to diagnose other ophthalmological problems. If my colleague detects signs of these she will advise the patient to see their doctor or an optician.

But to read the signals in the eye is to begin to decode all the body's messages. Everyone knows that pinkly veined whites may speak of a heavy night before and that a darkening of the iris sometimes indicates stress or anger. But each person's irises, left and right, can reveal information about the health and state of every organ, muscle and bone. Every fleck, speckle and thread of colour (dark or light) within your iris connects with some part of your body. My colleague says that when she was first confronted with the complexities of the eye map at the start of her year's training in iridology she doubted if she could ever remember all the subtleties. Now she can look you in the eye and, possibly without even taking a picture and enlarging it, locate a problem in the heart, lungs, kidney or bowel.

Iridology, now so crucial to my work, is a science which has been practised for thousands of years in sophisticated ancient civilizations. About a hundred years ago it began to be practised seriously and with respect in Germany, where it is now widely recognized as a vital and valuable discipline. Its merits have yet to be properly recognized in Britain, where the medical establishment remains wary of procedures which are not included in the training syllabuses. Even today there are only about 150 trained iridologists working in Britain.

But perhaps the science will come to enjoy the same form of acceptance as reflexology, which only a few years ago was still being dismissed by the British Medical Council but which is now employed, with notable success, in some of London's leading teaching hospitals. Cancer patients and pregnant mothers, in particular, are being helped. My iridologist colleague, who is also trained in anatomy and physiology, has helped many patients by locating blockages and organic deterioration that I have subsequently been able to release. Neither of us diagnoses: we observe and react but leave diagnosis to conventionally trained professionals. It is up to our patients to decide whether or not to return to us for further consultation. It is surely time that these healings and their methods became accepted; they are not only effective but are no particular drain on the public purse. Something as simple as a change of diet can correct things that may have taken many expensive consultations and dubious drug prescriptions to identify and only possibly resolve. In her own separate and independent practice my colleague, who is not a dowser, has had remarkable success with the combination of counselling, including advice related to stress, healing and the recommendation of herbal and organically based diets. She tells me that most iridologists also come to train as herbalists even if they have not acquired this expertise and skill beforehand.

There is no part of the body whose health or malfunction is not reflected in the iris. A little brown or yellow fibrous thread leading away from the pupil will shout clearly of a disorder and a trained iridologist can locate the root of a patient's trouble at once. With her report to hand I dowse the area which seems to be blocked or stressed and more often than not I am able to find the point in the patient's personal history when things were working fine in that department. Then I place the appropriate tablets on the body. Toxins will be drawn out and with luck a corrected diet will do the rest. How long this takes depends on the severity of the disorder.

Putting it at its simplest, I see the eyes rather like the dials of a clock or watch. At 'six o'clock' I can immediately see a specific problem in one area, at 'half-past eleven' I may spot another. The condition of every part of your body – colon, bladder, liver, nervous system, lungs, reproductive organs and skin surface – can be observed in the enlarged photographs of the two irises. Complicated as if may sound, the same map applies to everyone. We all display physical traits in the same specific and particular areas of our irises, so once one is familiar with the map it is relatively easy to generalize. The skills of an iridologist are not easily or quickly learned, but they are to be trusted. The eyes' records are invariably truthful if only they can be read. For example, a patient mentioned a number of niggling physical problems during an early consultation with my iridologist collegue but forgot to mention some severe recent back pains. But to the patient's surprise she immediately noticed evidence of them during her examination of the eyes and I was able to dowse away those back pains when I saw the patient later.

It astonishes me that conventional medicine still all but dismisses iridology. How extraordinary that such a natural gift, working so effectively without pain, drugs or hospitalization, should be seen at best as a challenge and at worst as a threat. Fast, comfortable and very often miraculously revealing, iridology is a science which must surely soon be taken seriously. The reports from my colleague not only supply invaluable short cuts in my subsequent dowsing-based treatments but also serve as proof, testing and double-checking that I am on the right track in pursuing my own methods.

Very often a hospital specialist will brim with pride when he or she notices a distinct improvement in a patient's condition, unaware that the patient has also been treated at my clinic and will have desisted from drugs prescribed earlier and elsewhere. The specialist might assume that their drugs have done the trick. I may take a little pride in my success and allow the hospital doctor to bask in the pleasure and credit that my patient's improvement has bestowed.

Marvellous though it is, I do not seek to claim that iridology can reveal disorders which would otherwise go unnoticed. Rather, it saves vital time, expense and discomfort in locating an area of physical or emotional stress and often leads to dowsing-divined treatments which can often alleviate the problem far more rapidly than conventional tests, experiments, surgery and drugs.

It is astounding, confounding and perhaps worrying to some that such hugely constructive work can be so simple. My colleague is a wonderfully calm person whose reassurance that there will be no discomfort or distress during the examination, however murky the eye may prove to be, is vital. Some patients will always worry so much about the painless bright light of the flash bulb that they won't be photographed. In these cases she simply takes a long, informed look at the eyes and can read them pretty clearly, if not in such precise detail as usual. The eyes of children, who can rarely sit still for the required hour, are usually studied in this way.

In fact most of her patients find the examination so soothing and relaxing that they find themselves speaking of emotional and physical problems unrelated to the trouble that brought them to the clinic in the first place and which they may have denied before. In her own private clinic she mainly and successfully treats such problems with reflexology, healing, herbalism and diet advice. Sometimes a simple change of diet is all that is required – but it takes a leap of faith and trust in the healer on the part of the patient.

My colleague studied iridology under a distinguished British lawyer who retrained in natural health therapies, including iridology, at the International Institute of Iris Diagnosis in Germany, after it had helped him overcome disorders that conventional medicine had failed to deal with. He then went on to become founder and president of the Canadian Institute of Iridology, and was clearly a good teacher . . . and so that good, beneficial wheel turns.

More recently, I discovered another method of diagnosis which helps me in my work.

Professor David Schweitzer has a clinic in London and one of his disciplines is cellular biology. He has the ability to diagnose any faults inside the cells of the blood. He achieves this with the aid of a microscope, a colour printer and a computer screen on which the blood sample can be displayed. The method he follows is to pinprick the tip of the little finger and smear five samples of blood on a test plate.

I visited Professor Schweitzer's surgery on 28 August 1997. He took the usual five smears of blood and placed the plate inside his powerful microscope. He calls this test the HLB test. This showed that I was suffering from slight anaemia and a lack of ability to assimilate food. I also had a parasite infection and I had a cancer cell in my blood. He also diagnosed that I was deficient in two essential amino acid proteins, methionine and cysteine. He graded my blood grade three, slightly higher than the lowest level, and advised me to take as supplements the two amino acids I was deficient in.

I was flabbergasted that my inner cells should be in such a state. I considered myself healthy – I felt well, and everybody always commented how well I looked. As a dowser I had a complete understanding of the state of my physical body as well as the organs and my systems and I kept them in a pretty good state of repair, but I had never actually analysed the blood in the way that Professor Schweitzer demonstrated. Dowsing is the knowledge of what to look for and the Professor certainly alerted me to look inside my own cells and track down the cause of the malfunction.

I analysed the components of my blood cells and found there was an element called astatine which I was not absorbing. I knew from past experience that each element and each nutrient that is in our system has to have six genes to ensure its general function. The genetic code says that each gene has to have four basic amino acid proteins for it to work. I found there was only one working on astatine; the other three were blocked. Dowsing also told me that without astatine there was no way I could absorb methionine. Further dowsing revealed that the reason why I could not absorb astatine was that the three coded letters were blocked by genetic copper poisoning inherited from both my mother's and my father's lines. Counting back, the cause originated nineteen generations ago on my father's side and eighteen generations ago on my mother's. They probably used copper pots or something similar and this poisoned their systems. I corrected this deficiency with a special formula which released astatine which then released my ability to absorb methionine.

On 9 December 1997, I returned to Professor Schweitzer for a fresh blood analysis. The plates showed quite clearly that the cancer had disappeared, the cells were normal, and the parasite had gone. My degenerative state had receded and my position on the ladder was now one. The test revealed that I had further work to do, as I still had not solved the deficiency of cysteine. I am grateful to Professor Schweitzer for alerting me to the importance of measuring each of the amino acid proteins that we must have working for us in our systems.

CHAPTER TWELVE

Journeys

In nature, all is balance. We all have a very simple choice: when the body seems to be letting us down we can succumb to decline or turn to nature to help us recover. The natural means is almost always the most effective, but that isn't to say that it is always the simplest . . .

I know absolutely that somewhere in our world there is a flower, plant, herb or mineral that can alleviate any pain, that can arrest or at least control illness, and repair any damage. But if a combination of several elements is needed for any one medicine I must take my time to find the correct mixture. If, for example, six different parts are needed to work together for the treatment, all my effort will be wasted if I try to settle for five. That is why I travel as I do and an open ticket flight is usually the first and easiest stage of my journey.

I always travel hopefully and I usually find those hopes fulfilled upon arrival. Along with my toothbrush I take an open mind and an open, curious and adventurous heart. I pack no allergies or prejudices, either.

I will have planned my journey much more carefully than someone who has leafed through the brochures and decided that this year it will be Italy, Canada or wherever. Without claiming that I do not often enjoy my travels and their recreational aspects, I don't plan trips with art, culture, fabulous cuisines, sunbathing or simple relaxation in mind: these are all bonuses if things work out that way. I'm not on holiday. Perhaps because of my enjoyment of life, work and good health, I don't *need* those recuperative breaks that so many other people do . . .

The pendulum will have told me where to go to seek the specific plant, mineral or flower source energies that I need to process and develop for a particular patient or a common malaise. In an extraordinary but frequent coincidence, an illness often afflicts a number of other patients around the same time. I might need to seek a remedy for a heart, respiratory, kidney or stomach problem common to more than one patient and the medicine derived can be used time and time again for many future patients. Sounds cheap? Remember that my consultations cost far less than the treatments prescribed because I have invested heavily in the time and expense needed to research, travel and eventually find, perhaps, a single leaf or stone.

Time has proved to me that whilst no one should put their faith and trust in instant cures, we should all accept that the humble-seeming forms of natural life – even repellent ones like worms or pests – can be our friends. Worms have perfect organic form, nourished by the earth, and some species have survived for thousands of years, thousands of miles away. Pests in 'exotic' regions may cause illness and pain but they too have thrived despite poorly cultivated or drained environments. We can learn from this. That which has allowed the pest to survive can be reversed to enable a human body to regenerate. And never forget that a rash, an itch or pain, perhaps caused by an insect-spread infection, is a friendly warning, alerting us to a bodily weakness and encouraging us to seek help. Without toothache there would be little dentistry (and many toothless mouths), without the sting in the foot people would not know that their body had been poisoned by a sea urchin or jelly fish, and without the flea bite millions would not be impelled to treat their homes, pets and selves against such intruders.

By now you will be familiar with the way that my dowser (which could as easily be a bunch of keys as a silver pendulum) will identify my destination as I hold it over a map, asking my usual questions. It has never yet directed me off on a pointless journey or wild-goose chase. And I'll know that the magnetic energy of whatever I find there, however minute the quantity I later distil, can be regenerated every time I shake the tiny phial.

I always book an open ticket so that there is no stopwatch on my search and when I arrive I check into a hotel and the dowsing begins again. I've long stopped expecting, or even hoping, to find 'cure-alls' and neither do I believe that the further I travel the better my chances will be. If the pendulum swings wildly over an apparently dull field only a few miles away from home I'm just as excited as if it has called me to Bali or the West Indies. I go wherever I am called.

Some time ago I was searching for a formula in Israel's West Bank and needed one more item to complete it. My taxi driver advised against proceeding as soldiers were nearby and gunshot was audible but I was determined to find that last leaf and I did. The resultant tincture has since been used to help hundreds of patients.

Wherever I am I will find a driver who is prepared to take me to the place I have dowsed on my local map. This might be in the town centre but is more often miles away in difficult terrain. I'm sure they sometimes think I'm barking mad and I seldom have the correct language to explain my purpose but on the whole I have found my local drivers to be helpful and tolerant. Often they have proved to be wise, as well. Once a local taxi driver, in Faro, Portugal, quite possibly baffled by the sight of an energetic but elderly passenger in the back seat of his cab, observing the attention I paid to the silver pendulum, obeying my sign-language directions as we headed ever further up a rutted road winding round blasted mountainside, braked his car. He seemed to know that we had reached the destination. Instead of following the track and branching into others for hours I obeyed *his* instincts, however motivated they may have been. Less than thirty yards away was a dry bush. As I approached it the pendulum began to swing steadily and then wildly as a single leaf was recognized. I was ready to go home, mission accomplished. That final leaf completed the total of five leaves and herbs I needed to regenerate patients' weakened muscles. I owe much to my driver that day but am no longer surprised by such events: they happen too often. Chance encounters with unlikely people do guide and lead towards the miraculous.

When I was in Mauritius I made a special point of visiting the main market to dowse the local herbs on display. The stall-keeper became very interested and asked me to find the herb that would help *him* most. When I selected a rare herb to strengthen his bronchials he was amazed as he did, indeed, have bronchial problems and found the herb I chose to be corrective. Then he dived behind his display and gave me two herbs, poc poc and chart, not on public display. On a later journey to the Pyrenees I found French blueberries, which proved to be the third ingredient I needed to make a perfect skin cleanser.

In every aspect of life we must remain as open to the instincts of others as we are to our own.

Speaking of miracles, I must repeat that if a person has had such serious injury that they have had a metal plate inserted into a shattered bone joint I cannot render that plate redundant. What I know I can do is to make the surrounding bones, muscles, tissues and ligaments strong enough to hold the plate in comfortable and functional place far longer and better than the drugs so often demanded after complicated surgery. Mending, revitalization and recovery of a traumatized system will thus be faster and more enduring and effective.

It's simply a question of strength and will. Mine and that of the patient. I see it as my job to help the patient recover theirs. Since I travel so widely it is sometimes assumed that I am guided by or blessed by some of the mystic spirits which influenced ancient and distant civilizations. I don't see it quite like that since I was told by a medium to work it out for myself and that is what I have been doing ever since. In the past, to be sure, people may have been helped by a benevolent guiding spirit, a healer imbued with a stored and then tapped well of marvellous power and knowledge. This particular medium's advice made me confident as well as practical: if I have a gift of some kind I am truly grateful for it and I do believe – without claiming to understand – in what is known as the fifth dimension. But I have no idea, and little interest in, where that gift may have come from. My work, you could say, is educated guesswork. My guidance comes from the physical, tangible things like the herbs and plants – wherever I find them. I think I have an inkling about how basic medicine can be found and stored but claim very little understanding of how instinctive healing knowledge can be bestowed.

So I have a severely practical, rather than spiritual, way of going about my work. Firstly: Can I help? Secondly: Do I have treatments available already? If not, where can I find them? Once I've determined this I pack my bag and book that ticket if need be, taking with me the hair and nail clippings of patients whom I especially hope to help. I may well pack a special pendulum made from a green Maltese opal encased in solid silver, not because it is a 'lucky' device, but simply because it is beautiful and a pleasure to use.

Often, and understandably, I am asked why the plant or mineral-based treatments that derive from my journeys far afield can't be replicated nearer home. The sad and inconvenient fact is that there is seldom any point in even attempting this. It is not just the plant, tree, stone or herbal matter that provides the healing but the specific magnetic aura of the soil that nourished the vital element. Earth in Norway is not same as earth in Northamptonshire. Climate and the time of year – the growing seasons – also influence my travels. A herb gathered on the Isle of Skye may be perfect for my purposes in June, but if I need that healing herb in January the pendulum will direct me elsewhere, probably somewhere far south of the UK.

Once in my hotel room I will begin to ask questions about the location I seek. 'Is it accessible?' is usually the first one. If the pendulum remains still and steady I can guess that the nearest place may be ravine or cliffside, so I must try again: I am not reckless about my own safety – the West Bank incident was something of an exception. I dowse for the nearest accessible area, holding the pendulum over the hair or nail clippings asking for specific directions. Right here, or left? until I reach the precise spot and ultimately the exact fragment of plant or mineral substance that has the magnetic energy and aura that I need. I think I can claim that in this way I don't unnecessarily disturb or damage any part of nature that is best left alone. Here is one way in which the paths of herbalism and homeopathy differ. The first often calls for many different distillations while the second requires very few and thus interferes less with nature's balance.

There are very few places where I will not go in pursuit of healing materials. I won't venture into a civil war zone again, and I don't travel to places where vaccinations are a condition of entry. There must be somewhere else, so I will dowse for it . . . Perhaps this seems fainthearted, but I can't help anyone else if I don't look after myself, and the key to my health, just like anyone else's, is the strength of my heart. Think of the body as a car: new wheels, chassis or upholstery won't make it move if the engine is dodgy. No real regeneration can take place until the heart is functioning properly, so I make no apology for looking after mine.

My family history of heart trouble is abysmal, as I have mentioned. My father, mother and three brothers all died from heart-related weakness. I had thought mine was OK until I received a strange call from Denise Jacobs, a medium. I had never met her so when she said I should look after my heart by taking belladonna and feverfew I thought she was a practical joker, but to establish her bona fides she reminded me that I had hurt my head on a brick wall four years previously – something she could not possibly have known without psychic power.

I certainly remembered that painful experience. My wife was seriously ill and could barely breathe. I could call neither doctor nor ambulance as my wife had a horror of both so in desperation I banged my head against a wall. I was in fact able to help my wife and in time she recovered but I never told anyone about the incident. Denise Jacobs' call made me both take better care of my heart and respect those who can speak from the 'other side'.

Even something as trivial as athlete's foot cannot be addressed without first checking on the working order of the vitals like heart, kidney and lungs. Just as pain is a sign or warning, fungal and bacterial problems, however simple they may seem, are always indicative of a deeper breakdown of the system, so I never take them lightly and I completely reject the idea that wishing to be in tune with the body by taking every symptom seriously is vanity.

If I can possibly help it I never stay away from my practice for more than a week. In Greece once, heading back towards the airport at Athens, I saw many ancient remains and was awestruck by the thought of the benefits brought to our civilization by the ancient Greeks. I pondered the sophistication of ancient civilizations and was really tempted to study the subject properly and delay my return to Britain – no problem, after all, with an open ticket. But my mission had been to find healing matter for people who were sick and suffering there, not to enjoy or indulge myself, so I stuck to my plan. The achievements of the ancient Greeks have survived for a very long time: they can wait a little while longer for me to visit someday when I am not on a healing mission.

Not all my dowsing relates directly to physical ailments. If I am convinced that the holistic health of a person could depend on the direction of a relationship or on a professional career choice, I see no paradox in dowsing for an answer, but such consultations are much less likely to lead me to distant fields. There is almost nowhere in the world my pendulum has not led me in search of healing for more recognizably physical problems, but dowsing can also pick up and expose a person's deepest, almost buried intuitive feelings about something that may be troubling them enough to manifest in physical breakdown. For example, if a patient has a choice of six career moves I get them to write down the name of each one, and cover all the names but one. Then I place my finger on the patient's sternum, about three inches down from the centre, and dowse the uncovered name, repeating for each name in turn. My pendulum will swing in accordance with the patient's deepest, instinctive wishes. The answers sometimes surprise but the name which causes the pendulum to swing most wildly gives my patient a lead or a choice. True friends and false can be identified in the same way. The answers may prove uncomfortable but patients have been known to resolve emotional dilemmas in this way.

On a much less serious note, I once wanted to buy my wife a handbag as a present during a trip to Cyprus. I had the shopkeeper line up fifteen of them and then I started to dowse. Holding up a sample of my wife's hair and with a finger on my thymus, my eyes lighted on each bag in turn. I bought the bag which brought the greatest pendulum response. She was delighted with it. I once bought her a coat using the same method – that too was a winner.

This isn't trivial. Our intuitive brain is very wise and we should never deny or ignore its messages. It helps to create or restore harmony in our lives. Colour plays its part in this and it is very important in my work. Indeed, it is important in all of our lives. We all respond differently to colour, light and shade, and our responses can vary with age and health as well as fashion and taste. The colours we choose to wear or use in our homes are much more than a shallow, fashion-influenced whim. Men as well as women favour particular colours to wear, knowing which ones do or do not suit them. They express something inside that we feel at ease with, which is why it is often a great mistake for a friend or partner to pick clothing for another. Unless they are exceptionally in tune with the other person (or have a dowser to hand) the choice is as likely to generate disharmonious items as pleasurable ones.

The decision about the colour of paint or paper in the drawing room, the towels and bedlinen, even the shade of the flowers on the table or the car in the garage is usually a considered one. It must only be a short step to recognize that colour can affect our health as well.

The spectrum of colours that I work with adheres pretty much to the colours of the rainbow. The plants and stones which I dowse, whilst by no means always stridently bright, always have elements of brown, orange, yellow, green, red and blue in them. Different colours generate different types of ionization or energy and that energy can be identified, isolated and utilized in my treatments. My research in this field was greatly helped by a book on colour therapy – now sadly out of print – by Dr Reuben Amber, but many books are now available on healing with colour. Very simply, the list below indicates how certain colours (many of them found in stones and crystals, of course) can influence the relief of specific ailments.

yellow	liver problems, depression
orange	asthma, mental exhaustion
green	blood pressure, problems of the nervous system
blue	gastrointestinal problems, itches and rashes
red	blood ailments, stress
indigo	ear problems, lung problems
violet	bladder problems, cramps

So trust your instincts if you want to wear yellow one day and blue or green the next. Your brain and bones are probably advising you to reach for something of the colour whose signals and energies will be good for you that day. I always use the thymus gland and my eyes to choose colours that I feel comfortable with. I simply place a left finger slightly to the right of my centre chest, on the sternum, and look at the colour in question. If it's the right one for whatever purpose I have in mind the pendulum will swing vigorously.

Dowsing is like learning Latin. We start on the simple verbs, nouns, adjectives, etc. and by repetition these are firmly stored in the brain to be retrieved as needed. Dowsing works in exactly the same way. The more one dowses the greater is the strength of the brain to acquire, store and remember this new skill.

Over the years of my work and travelling I have come to recognize this ever more clearly. The successes derived from so many of my journeys have depended so often on chance encounters and unlikely situations that I now have complete trust in my intuitions. Dowsing is sometimes merely a different way of clarifying one's hunches and being receptive to them. The pendulum is not, after all, some independent free spirit. It is your tool and your means of telling you things you probably already knew, deep down.

Conclusions

I've seen a lot of changes over the years, a good many of them for the better, and on the scale of things I would say that these outweigh my regret about some of the deplorable things which have emerged in the name of 'progress'.

In any case, only a fool would attempt to stem the march or tide of progress: the trick is to learn from it and to see how often, ironically, modern thinking can make us constructively re-evaluate the past.

Over time alternative healers like me have been both feared and fashionable, derided and overpraised, exploited and exploitative, and used, abused, copied and forgotten. In my own working life I've experienced many of these reactions.

I'm now used to this, and to adverse comments as well as praise – and I'm always ready to learn something new if it will help me with my work, so I always treat constructive criticism with respect. And anything that I have ever learned that is worth remembering will be conveyed to the younger ones who study with me and plan to set up healing centres of their own.

Nature, of course, never forgets. Those trees outside my window will stand for hundreds of years yet and eventually bequeath their memories of survival to the soil. The stones which I can also see will last eternally. The sea waters which lap every one of the earth's shores will remain powerful enough to cleanse themselves of most of the filth that is dumped into their depths and supply essential elements for human survival. In every field of endeavour people have adapted to change and risen to a challenge.

I remain extremely optimistic. The more I learn the more I realize that there is still much to be discovered that can benefit human healing. This is exciting. Healers of the past were often mocked yet today their discoveries frequently form the basis of some of the world's most enlightened and effective health research. If this thinking eventually seeps into commercially produced products, so be it. Business has always been an aspect of human survival, from the time when the caveman who first learned that rubbing two sticks or flints together could create warmth and a fire and invited his neighbour round to supper – providing the neighbour brought the food. Or bartered a special healing herb from his patch for a special bone tool from his hunter neighbour.

It's sometimes called enlightened self-interest – this intelligent utilization of what we have been given by the environment, which is often staring us in the face. Call it trade, commerce, call it what you will: it is all part of our species' instinct for survival and it often has the happy knock-on effect of preserving and encouraging the growth of non-human life forces.

No one is forced to consult me, or to come back after their first visit. They choose. I don't advertise and I can only assume that personal recommendation has caused my clinic to flourish and others like mine to spring up. I am always glad to wave a patient away if it seems I have helped them after only one visit, and it is sometimes with mixed feelings that I greet them if they return years later. But I have to conclude that they were satisfied with my work and advice first time around and have come back, with faith, when something else has begun to trouble them. This is usually the case, and in the intervening years I will certainly have acquired new skills.

Only a few years ago I didn't know how to harness the power of auras or appreciate the importance of iridology. There were places in the world I had barely heard of, let alone visited, until my pendulum guided me there and led me to some special flower, seed or stone. There's still so much to learn, to distil and to utilize against modern disorders. Illness, of course, evolves as well as healing . . .

Patients of every age and type, at every stage and type of problem, have been helped at my clinic. Their confidence in me is inspiring and their results – for I never forget that I am merely a conduit in the restoration of the good health they deserve – in turn inspire me.

And so the circle turns and the cycle is repeated. We can turn that wheel forward instead of accepting a backward, downward spiral or resorting to artificial 'aids' which create their own disorders. And we can do so naturally, with the help of all the good things that grown in the earth, stand on it or live in the surrounding seas.

All it needs is a little time, trust and faith.

Useful Addresses

AUSTRALIA

National Association for Sustainable
   Agriculture Australia Ltd
PO Box 768
Stirling
South Australia
SA 5152
Tel: 6208 370 8455
Fax: 6208 370 8381

Australian Federation of
   Homeopaths
238 Ballarat Road
Footscray
Victoria 3011
Tel: 03 9318 3057

Australian Institute of Homeopathy
7 Hampden Road
Artemon - 2064
Sydney
New South Wales 2064

CANADA

Certified Organic Products Inc
Box 609
Ituna
Saskatchawan
S0A 1N0
Tel: 306 795 3188
Fax: 306 795 3363

Canadian Society of Homeopathy
87 Meadowlands Drive West
Nepean
Ontario
K2G 2RP

Society of Iridologists (Canada)
Suite 18
2550 Golden Ridge Road
Mississauga
Ontario L4DX 2SA

The Canadian Institute of Iridology
2500 Bathurst Street
Suite 201
Toronto
Ontario M6B 2YB

NEW ZEALAND

Biological Producers Council
   (BIOGRO)
PO Box 36-170
Northcote
Auckland 9
Tel: 9 443 8435
Fax: 9 443 8436

New Zealand Homeopathic Society
Box 2929
Auckland
Tel: 9 630 9458

UNITED KINGDOM

The British Society of Dowsers
Sycamore Barn
Tamley Lane
Hastingleigh
Ashford
Kent TN25 5HW
Tel: 01233 750253

Scottish Organic Producers
    Association Ltd (SOPA)
Milton of Cambus
Doune
Perthshire FK16 6HG
Scotland
Tel/Fax: 01786 841657

The Soil Association
Bristol House
40-56 Victoria Street
Bristol BS1 6BY
Tel: 0117 929 0661

United Kingdom Register of Organic
    Food Standards (UKROFS)
MAFF, ARP Division
Room 323
Nobel House
17 Smith Square
London
SW1P 3JR
Tel: 0171 238 6004
Fax: 0171 238 6553

British Homoeopathic Association
27a Devonshire Street
London W1N 1RJ
Tel: 0171 935 2163

International Association of Clinical
    Iridology
853 Finchley Road
London NW11 8LX

UNITED STATES

Organic Crop Improvement
    Association International (OCIA)
3185 TWP RD 179
Bellefonteine
Ohio 43311
Tel: 513 592 4983
Fax: 513 593 3831

International Foundation for
    Homeopathy
2366 Eastlake Avenue
East Suit 301
Seattle
WA 98102
Tel: 206 776 4147

National Center for Homeopathy
801 N. Fairfax Street
Suite 306
Alexandria
Virginia 22314
Tel: 703 548 7790

National Iridology Research
    Association
PO Box 33637
Seattle
WA 98133

Society of Iridologists (USA)
10551 West Broward Boulevard
Apt 311
Plantation
Florida

Index

For *further information, please contact:*

Jack Temple Healing Centre
Pyrford Road
Pyrford
Woking GU22 8UQ
England, UK
Tel 01932 342429
Fax 01932 800300
e-mail:info@jacktemple.co.uk
website: www.jacktemple.co.uk

For a complete Findhorn Press catalogue, please contact:

Findhorn Press

The Press Building, The Park, Findhorn,
Forres IV36 3TY
Scotland, UK
Tel 01309 690582
freephone 0800-389-9395
Fax 01309 690036
e-mail info@findhornpress.com
www.findhornpress.com